⚓ ⚓ ⚓ ⚓

Now, Hear This!

by the same author

CLEAR THE DECKS

TWENTY MILLION TONS UNDER THE SEA

NOW, HEAR THIS!

by Daniel V. Gallery,

Rear Admiral USN (Ret.)

Introduction by Herman Wouk

W · W · NORTON & COMPANY · INC · New York

Contents

Introduction

by Herman Wouk

DANIEL V. GALLERY is a writer of humor and adventure who somehow got diverted into becoming an admiral of the line in the United States Navy.

Admirals are not, as a body, celebrated for humor. Skill with words in a naval man of flag rank is a foible best concealed. But Gallery has been indiscreetly publishing amusing tales, true narratives, and polemical essays for many years. If his active naval career survived public display of his literary facility, it can only have been because he happened to be an outstanding officer.

The exploit of Gallery's anti-submarine task group, in boarding and capturing the U-boat 505 in mid-Atlantic, is famous. The U-boat now sits—ugly, incongruous, evilly fascinating—on dry land outside the Museum of Science and Industry in Chicago, a grim relic of Nazism, a memento of Gallery's will power, and most of all a monument to the ingenuity and bravery of the American seamen who brought off the historic adventure.

To have even conceived of this feat—boarding a surfaced, damaged enemy submarine; closing the scuttle valves, finding and disarming the demolition charges in the few minutes before they would blow up and sink submarine and boarders alike; and then

Introduction

towing the prize home to disembowel it of its precious wartime secrets—surely this was not the brainchild of a conventional fighting man. But to think up a wild sea adventure is one thing; to enact it on the high seas, amid the hazards of wind, wave, and enemy action, at the risk of many lives, with brilliant success, is another. Gallery's wartime know-how was equal to his imagination.

This imagination has expressed itself in many bizarre ways. Gallery's realistic tin palm trees around his flag base in Iceland have become a naval legend. One of Gallery's last active duty posts was at the Naval Base in San Juan, Puerto Rico, as Commander of the Caribbean Sea Frontier. Besides his multifarious official duties (I once saw this rainbow-bemedalled sea dog and jet pilot grimly stepping through a Puerto Rican square dance, with the lady mayor of San Juan as his partner), the Admiral brought into being the famed Navy Steel Band. A steel band produces exotic Caribbean music by the pounding of sticks on sawed-off oil drums. The first time the Admiral saw one of these native groups he called in his band-master and asked him why American sailors couldn't make such drums and learn to play them. "Admiral Dan's Pandemoniacs" have since played all over the United States and in foreign capitals. Gallery also had a young sailor in the band learn to dance the limbo. I saw the lad pass under the bar at a lower setting than any native performer I have ever watched.

In Fleet Admiral Ernest King's biography, the gruff wartime leader is sparing of references to other officers. But he mentions Daniel Gallery several times with clear regard, and a tinge of amusement. This must be the general navy view of Rear Admiral Daniel V. Gallery, U.S.N. (Ret.). He is a true original. His career is proof that—the prevalence of organization men notwithstanding—an original can make a first-class fighting man.

They used to say that Ernie King was so tough he shaved with a blowtorch. When he passed through Gallery's domain during the war, he probably borrowed Gallery's torch. It may have even given

8

King's granite chin a few nicks. Gallery is soft-spoken as admirals go. But when a rare snafu occurs under his command, the smell of brimstone in his vicinity is bloodcurdling.

These random notes on the wintry, wiry author of the tall tales in this volume may serve to give the reader a little extra pleasure in reading the yarns. Truthfulness is forced on an admiral, in his official character. While I wouldn't exactly accuse Daniel Gallery of a frustrated taste for lying (not unless I had a clear road and a good head start), there is an unmistakable exuberance in the improbability of his sea stories. Admiral Dan has a high old time letting himself go and prevaricating to his heart's content in the fictional adventures of Fatso Gioninni, Beer Bottle, Satchelaft, and all his other light-hearted and light-fingered characters. Such pleasure is contagious to the reader.

When reserve scribblers like the author of *Mr. Roberts* and myself reported similar goings-on in the Navy, we were sometimes censured for libeling a flawless and peerless service. Admiral Daniel V. Gallery makes it official, in this volume, that sailors are human beings, and moreover, that Admirals are, too. Anybody who likes funny, salt-encrusted sea stories, told with vivid and absolute authenticity of Navy detail, and with an outrageous disregard for all other aspects of the truth, will have a grand time with this book.

Herman Wouk

AUTHOR'S NOTE

I resent Mr. Wouk's implication, or more accurately, his flat statement, that this book is a pack of lies. At least one of the incidents related herein happened exactly the way I tell it. (Well—*almost* exactly anyway.)

Besides, it is a well-known fact that in telling a sea story you have to exaggerate a little bit, otherwise landlubbers wouldn't believe it.

⚓ ⚓ ⚓ ⚓

Now, Hear This!

⚓ CHAPTER ONE

"Trash" Disposal Problem

IN THE CABIN of the giant aircraft carrier *Okinawa*, at sea with the Sixth Fleet in the Mediterranean, the Captain and Executive Officer were discussing a matter of high-level ship's policy.

"He's getting away with murder, Cap'n," said the Commander.

"No doubt about that, Joe," said the Captain; "but—just what do you propose to do about it?"

"I'm not proposing to do anything, Captain," said the Commander. "I just want to be sure you know what the score is."

"I know what the score is all right," said the Captain rather ruefully. "My bones would have been on the bottom of the Pacific Ocean for the past twenty years if it wasn't for that crafty scoundrel. And I think the score is about the same for you as it is for me —isn't it, Joe?"

"It sure is," said the Exec. "He dragged me out of a burning plane on the *Yorktown* at the battle of Midway just before it blew up."

The subject of this discussion was one John Patrick Gioninni, Bosun's Mate 1/c, and a veteran of over twenty years' more or less faithful naval service beginning just before World War II. It had been very faithful indeed whenever bombs and torpedoes were exploding, but no more faithful than necessary at other times.

"So—," said the Captain, "What do we do now?"

"I guess we just keep on covering up for the guy," said the Exec.

"We can't do much else," agreed the Captain, "and after all, that isn't too tough a job. He covers up for himself so well that most of the time we never even hear about it, except when some over-zealous young officer, who never got his life saved by him, butts in and louses things up for him. And the stuff he is getting away with is within reason—or at least *almost* within reason—most of the time."

"That's right," agreed the Commander. "And you know, Captain, he's really a good influence on the ship, that is if you don't count what he and his pals get away with. He's a stickler for regulations as far as the younger sailors are concerned. He never puts anybody on report, but if any monkey business gets started on the ship that's bad for discipline, outside of his own activities, he can stop it quicker than anyone else on board."

"Right," agreed the Captain. "And if fire broke out in the magazines he and his mob would be the ones you could really depend on to go down there and put it out."

"I suppose it's just one of the aftermaths of the war that we have to learn to live with," said the Exec philosophically. "But I often wish it was okay for Commanders to play tricks on sailors. I know a dozen ways I could booby-trap that guy—but good!"

"I know what you mean," said the Captain wistfully. "If I ever run across him after I retire . . ."

While this conversation was going on in the cabin, the man on whom the discussion focused, "Fatso" Gioninni, BM1c, was taking life easy in the incinerator compartment several decks below on the starboard side of the hangar deck.

Fatso was Captain of the Incinerator on the *Okinawa*, a job corresponding roughly to head of the city dump ashore. All he had to do was to burn up the trash that accumulates on a big ship and which can't be thrown overboard, because in wartime you don't want to leave a trail of rubbish behind you indicating to the enemy where you have been, or even more importantly, where you may be going.

You may wonder why an experienced petty officer like Fatso was assigned such a minor military mission as running the incinerator. On most ships, this job is given to a boot seaman, rather than a first class bosun's mate with four hashmarks on his sleeve.

As a matter of fact, it was a scandalous waste of manpower to put a man of Fatso's talent on this job. Fatso was one of those real sailormen who are rapidly becoming extinct in this modern mechanized Navy. He knew all there was to know about practical seamanship, such as how to run the foc'sle when anchoring or getting underway, how to rig for fueling at sea, how to lower or pick up the ship's boats in heavy weather, and all the many other jobs peculiar to a ship which require a seaman's eye and knowledge of wind and wave even in the atomic age. If something went wrong with your fire-control radar you would call on the double-domed electronic technicians to fix it. But if they said that before they could work on it you had to unship that big radar dish from the top of the mast and lower it down to the flight deck, then Fatso was your man.

But Fatso wasn't at all embarrassed at devoting his great talents to the humble job of running the incinerator. His philosophy of life was very simple. He had swum away from three ships that got sunk under him during the war and had decided that since he was now living on borrowed time he would live the full life until the loan was called. He figured that between wars his duty to his country was to preserve the unique skills and experience he had acquired and to keep them sharp and ready for instant use when the next war broke out. Obviously the best way to do this was to avoid overworking himself, or being subjected to severe mental or physical strain. So Fatso had put in for this incinerator job and, on the U.S.S. *Okinawa,* any reasonable request made by Fatso got a fair hearing at the top level. Both the skipper and the Exec knew that Fatso's request for the incinerator was outrageously unreasonable and that there must be an angle to it—but—what could they do?

The angle to the incinerator job was that it provided Fatso with privacy, and privacy was essential for most of Fatso's activities. Tucked away in the after end of the island on the starboard side of the hangar deck, the roomy incinerator compartment made an ideal headquarters for Fatso and his cronies. Most compartments on a ship are more or less public places where sailors come and go. Not so the incinerator compartment. Sailors brought trash there from all over the ship but they never saw the inside of the place. They dumped their trash in a big bin which could be emptied through a trap door inside the compartment. Nobody ever got into the inner sanctum except Fatso, his pals, and on inspections, the Admiral or Captain.

So a lot of things went on in the big furnace room which at first glance might not seem to be strictly in accordance with the U.S. Navy regulations. But Fatso took a tolerant view of the regulations, realizing that they were intended to prescribe a way of life for the farm hands, shoe clerks, and juvenile delinquents who were enlisting in the Navy these days—not for oldtimers like him. He knew all the Regulations by heart, and also the devious ways of getting around them. The last time he had been busted from Chief to 1st class it had been due to just plain sloppy work by his defense counsel at the court-martial, rather than to any fault of Fatso's.

Fatso was perfectly willing to die for his country in wartime if necessary but he didn't propose to put up with any horsefeathers for it in peacetime.

This afternoon when our story opens, he was relaxing in a "borrowed" ward-room easy chair with his feet up on a locked sea chest, which was loaded with liquor. A young volunteer helper, one Willy Watts, was doing the manual labor of shoveling trash into the blazing furnace, while Fatso held him spellbound with tales of the South Pacific when Admiral Halsey was in charge there. As Fatso concluded the outrageous lie he had been telling about one of the great sea battles of World War II, Willy remarked:

"I see you got a Navy Cross with a gold star in it on that dress uniform hanging in your locker over there, Fatso."

"Yeah," said Fatso. "Got 'em during the war."

"Gee!" said Willy. "Two Navy Crosses! There weren't many sailors who got *one* Navy Cross, let alone two of them."

"Aw, they handed them out by the bucketful during the war," said Fatso modestly. "In the Pacific, anyway."

"What did you get them for?" asked Willy.

"Just for being around when things got noisy," replied Fatso.

"I don't believe that. What did you do, Fatso?"

"Well if you *must* know," replied Fatso, "one was for the Captain and the other for the Exec."

"How do you mean?"

"I got sunk on the *Lexington* with the Captain and on the *Yorktown* with the Exec. I swum around holding the Captain up for a while after the *Lexington* got sunk and I helped the Exec get out of a burning plane on the *Yorktown*. So Admiral Halsey gave me a couple of medals. Admiral Halsey just *loved* to hand out medals."

"You mean the Captain and Exec of *this* ship?" asked Willy.

"Yeah," said Fatso. "They was just ensigns then and didn't know how to take care of themselves very well."

"I can see now where you get your drag on *this* ship," observed Willy.

"Whaddya mean, drag?" demanded Fatso indignantly. "I ain't got no drag on this ship. I'm just like any other sailor on this bucket. I keep my nose clean and do my job the same as the rest of you guys should. The only way to get a drag in this Navy is to do your duty as best you can and abide by the regulations," he added piously—bracing his feet against the liquor chest and shoving it a little further into the corner.

"Uh huh," said Willy dubiously.

"You sound kinda doubtful, son," said Fatso.

"Well . . . I dunno, Fatso . . . I know lots of regulations that don't seem to bother you much."

"That's because I'm *used* to them," explained Fatso. "And I know what they really mean, not just what's down there in black and white in the regulation book."

"I don't get that," said Willy.

"The Regulations," explained Fatso, "are written for people who wouldn't know what to do when something comes up unless they had a book to tell them. Usually there are at least a couple of ways of doing anything, but the book only gives you the simplest way so any dumb cluck can do it. If you're new in the Navy the safest way is to follow the book so you know you can't be wrong. But after you've put in twenty years or so and know your way around it's OK to do it one of the other ways." ("If you don't get caught . . ." he added under his breath.)

Next morning as the *Okinawa* ploughed through the blue waters of the Mediterranean toward the harbor of Naples, squawk boxes all over the ship blared forth the bugle call "Assembly." On the last note of the bugle there was a long shrill blast of the bosun's pipe, followed by the word "Now hear this. All hands bring ship to anchor! Fall in at your quarters on the flight deck, all divisions!"

For the next five minutes the *Okinawa* resembled Grand Central Station during the rush hour as thousands of sailors came trooping up from the living compartments and lined up on the flight deck facing outboard.

Down below the masters-at-arms prowled through the ship, clearing the lower decks of stragglers and checking the alibis of sailors

"Trash" Disposal Problem

who claimed they were excused from quarters. On the hangar deck a harsh voice snarled, "Come on you swab jockeys . . . drag it out of here . . . haul your ass up to the flight deck . . . get moving you guys."

The petty officer who issued these orders out was one "Commissar" Jones, master-at-arms of the hangar deck, and a character who was not universally beloved by the crew of the *Okinawa*. He was always ear-banging with the officers and he would put his own grandmother on the report if he thought he could do himself any good by it. He could count his friends among the 3,000 men in the crew of the *Okinawa* on the thumbs of one hand.

The masters-at-arms are the ship's police, and of course no master-at-arms who is worth a damn will ever win a popularity contest among the crew. But Commissar carried this idea to extremes. He had a chip on both shoulders all the time and snooped around stirring up trouble even when he wasn't on duty.

But nobody in his right mind gets tough with a master-at-arms. So his belligerent attitude went unchallenged by the long-suffering sailors who were unfortunate enough to come under his jurisdiction.

Up on the bridge the Executive Officer surveyed the flight deck with a critical eye as chaos evolved into order, and the long lines of sailors in immaculate white uniforms and hats straightened out. The Marine Guard, looking as proud as only Marines can look in their parade uniforms, fell in up forward on the starboard side next to the band ready to render honors appropriate to the formal entry of a U.S. man-of-war to a foreign port.

"They look pretty good today," mused the Commander to himself as the last division snapped to attention. "I wonder what that eagle-eyed old buzzard over on the *Dover* will find to squawk about this time?" The U.S.S. *Dover*, flagship of the U.S. Mediterranean Fleet, was already at anchor in Naples, and "that eagle-eyed old buzzard" was of course the Admiral in command of the U.S. Mediterranean Fleet.

While all this hustle and bustle was going on throughout the ship, Fatso settled back comfortably in his armchair in the privacy of the incinerator compartment down on the hangar deck. One of the prerogatives that went with the incinerator job was that Fatso didn't have to attend quarters. So while everyone else on the ship hustled up to the flight deck in their best white uniforms, Fatso relaxed happily in a ragged suit of dungarees and a baseball cap. He sat there in his inner sanctum with a big cigar in his face, a comic book in one hand, and a cold bottle of beer in the other, at peace with the world.

A tardy sailor on his way up to the flight deck stuck his head in a port, and yelled, "Hey Fatso, gimme a number in the anchoring pool—make it snappy."

Out of sight behind the incinerator Fatso called out, "Sorry bub —all sold out . . . and there's no sale this close to the anchorage anyway—better get up there on deck before Commissar Jones lowers the boom on you."

This was indeed a bad morning to be late getting up on deck. A capital ship making a formal entry into a foreign port is like a duchess entering the throne room to be presented at court, and must observe a time-honored naval ritual involving a lot of high-level protocol. Several foreign men-of-war as well as the U.S.S. *Dover* were already at anchor in Naples, and from these ships scores of officers would be peering through binoculars and spyglasses alert to detect any deviation from the hallowed ritual. The skipper of the *Okinawa* was determined that there would be no deviation, and that his ship's arrival in the famous Bay of Naples would be a smart, seamanlike one, reflecting credit on the United States, and also of course on the captain of the *Okinawa*.

Elsewhere throughout the ship sailors heaved around with the customary preparations for anchoring. On the gallery walkway the

"Trash" Disposal Problem

Chief Gunner and the saluting gun crews were breaking out enough blank ammunition for a twenty-one-gun national salute to the Republic of Italy and personal salutes to the Italian, French, British, and American admirals. It was the gunner's job to fire exactly the number of shots which time-honored usage demanded in each case, with the "booms" spaced precisely 5 seconds apart.

"You gun captains watch me for your firing signals and bang 'em off promptly," he said, "and in case of a misfire don't stand around picking your noses and wondering what to do. Shift to the standby gun and go ahead as if nothing had happened."

Up on the bridge the signal floozies broke out Italian, French, and British flags and got them ready to run up to the masthead during the firing of salutes. The Chief Signalman cocked a seaman's eye aloft to see that there were no Irish pennants in the rigging and that all the bunting was properly two-blocked.

At the bow, a quartermaster made the jack up into a little ball, wrapped the halyards around it and ran it up to the top of the staff so that when the anchor went down all he had to do was jerk one halyard and the flag would break out in its proper position. In deference to Old Eagle Eye on the *Dover*, he carefully checked when he hooked the jack on that it would break out with the points of the stars up. Maybe you think it doesn't make much difference which way you hoist a flag like the jack, but it makes a lot of difference if Old Eagle Eye is in the same port.

Back on the fantail two other quartermasters stood by ready to run up the big set of U.S. colors when the mud hook went down and the flag had to shift aft from its underway position at the mainmast. You can't wad the national colors into a ball and break them out as you do the jack—you must *hoist* them and they must never be allowed to touch the deck. So one quartermaster held the flag in his arms and the other hooked on and manned the halyards. Both had double-checked that the *hoisting* halyard was the one

Now, Hear This!

hooked into the grommet in the blue field. There was that never-to-be-forgotten day in Gibraltar when poor old Dopey Dugan, formerly a quartermaster but now a seaman, had made naval history by smartly hoisting the national colors upside down!

At many other stations throughout the ship scores of sailors stood by to do the other things which must be done when the ship comes to anchor. The gangways must go down, the boat booms must swing out, and the boat cranes must lower away with the gig and barge. All of these things must happen at once—as if actuated by the running-out of the great anchor chain itself. Among naval men in peacetime these are the things on which a ship's reputation can stand or fall and woe betide the unlucky sailor who louses up the act by handling a line in a lubberly fashion.

All this high-level stuff means little to the ordinary sailors but on this particular morning many seamen were vitally interested in the forthcoming anchoring. This interest, however, had nothing to do with the prestige of the United States.

Up forward on the flight deck a bandsman said out of the corner of his mouth to a marine standing next to him:

"What number ya got in the anchoring pool, soldier?"

The marine cocked a wary eye at the top sergeant and said without moving his lips:

"Ten and a half—but it's 3 bucks down the scuppers now." (It was already 5 minutes after the hour and the ship wouldn't anchor for at least another 20 minutes.)

"I got 23," said the piccolo player hopefully. "Boy, what a liberty I can make to Rome if I hit that six-hundred-dollar jackpot."

Down on the foc'sle, just below the marine guard and band, the Chief Bosun and his gang were wrestling with the giant anchor chains, forged from steel bars as big around as your arm, getting the anchors ready for letting go. The ground tackle that holds a 60,000-ton ship securely moored against wind and tide is heavy gear. It takes hairy-chested sailormen to handle it and a salty seaman to boss the job. The Bosun was generally believed to have served as an apprentice boy with Noah in the Ark.

"Cast off them sea stoppers," he ordered. "Walk back handsomely on yer wildcat brakes . . . and you two (blank blank) Market Street Commandos on the brakes pay attention to my signals after we let go." (If you throw your weight around on a wildcat brake and try to snub a ship like the *Okinawa* up short by brute strength after the hook digs in you can easily tear the whole wildcat out by the roots.)

Husky seamen wrangled the stoppers off the chains leaving the 30-ton anchors suspended by the giant pelican hooks which gripped the chains just inboard of the 5-fathom shots. When the word was passed to "Let go," all you had to do now was to yank on the lanyard that pulled the preventer pin, clout the shackle on the pelican hook with a 10-pound sledge and then get the hell out of the way before that chain took a leg off just below your armpit.

When these preparations were completed the bosun's mate of the foc'sle said to the Bosun:

"Boats—how's to let someone else swing the sledge this morning? I've got a good number coming up in the anchoring pool and I don't want nobody to say there was nothing phony . . ."

"Okay," said the Bosun, who knew all the angles on anchoring pools in which seconds can decide the winner of a lot of money. Not even the Bosun himself could guarantee to knock that big shackle off the pelican hook every time with the first swing, and it was best not to have a man swinging the sledge who could—if he wanted to—use up quite a few seconds making false swings. This was simply following the precedent of the Supreme Court, where Justices disqualify themselves from cases in which they have a personal interest.

However, not everyone on the *Okinawa* had the ethical standards of a Supreme Court Judge and the hangar-deck master-at-arms,

Now, Hear This!

Commissar Jones, was one of those who didn't. At this very moment Jones was engaged in a nefarious enterprise smacking of both blackmail and piracy. He was putting the squeeze on the Navigator's yeoman, who typed the ship's log, and whom Jones had caught red-handed forging liberty cards, an offense which would certainly have cost him his rate if Jones reported him.

"All right kid," said Jones. "I'm not writing you up for this *yet*. You want to keep that crow on your arm and I don't want to take it away from you. But I've got 28 in the anchoring pool this morning and it's going to be pretty close to that time when we drop the hook. Just remember that when you write up the smooth log."

This proposition of Commissar Jones struck at the very roots of naval discipline and morale. It amounted to about the same thing as bribing the Government Printer to falsify the Congressional Record. Since a lot of money changes hands on the time of anchoring there is always argument about the exact second when the mud hook went down. This time is determined by stop watch on the bridge and is entered in the rough log at the moment of anchoring by the quartermaster on watch. But since the rough log is kept in pencil and is subject to change, and human nature being what it is, on a well-run ship they pay off the anchoring pool on the time recorded in the smooth log as signed by the Captain. This log is an official document of the United States, like the Constitution, and you certainly can't put in a fix with the Captain. But Commissar Jones now had the heat on the one weak link in the system —the yeoman who typed up the smooth log for the Captain's signature. This yeoman was not really a bad kid . . . but . . . he had worked hard for that crow on his arm.

Up on the bridge, as the ship steamed toward the harbor, the Navigator bent over an anchorage chart busily plotting the dope called in to him by his assistants who had their eyes glued to peloruses shooting bearings on the lighthouse, a prominent clock tower ashore, and the left tangent to a small island. Working with all deliberate haste he continuously pinpointed the ship's position, the Chief Quartermaster peering anxiously over his shoulder, stop watch in hand, announcing the time every 15 seconds and double-checking every bearing that the Navigator laid down on the chart. Periodically the Navigator called out the course and distance to the anchorage. "Zero four zero—one thousand yards, sir," he sang out as the saluting guns began banging away.

The Captain, out on the open bridge, kept one ear cocked toward the navigator and scanned the water ahead. Fishing boats, bumboats, and tugs with scows in tow permitting, this would be a bold approach, barging right up to the anchorage at good speed and dropping the hook right smack in the hole with no indecisive backing and filling.

A minute later the Captain said "all engines astern two thirds" and the ship began to tremble as the screws dug in. The Navigator's voice assumed an urgent pitch as he called out "400 yards, sir . . . 200 yards, sir . . ." A note of alarm crept in as he called out "75 yards, sir . . . closing rapidly."

"All engines back full speed," said the Captain. "Let go the starboard anchor."

A husky sailor on the foc'sle clouted the shackle on the pelican hook and scrambled clear as the 30-ton anchor plunged to the bottom and the great chain crashed across the deck and down the hawsepipe. The whole ship quaked as the engine room shot the steam to the astern turbines, and the Bosun up on the foc'sle goggled over the side at the headway and waved at the brakeman on the wildcat to let her run!

Down in the incinerator compartment Fatso took another swig of his beer and noted that by his watch they had anchored at exactly 25 minutes and 18 seconds after the hour. Running the anchoring pool was one of Fatso's many extracurricular rackets—although the way he ran it, it wasn't really a racket at all. He only kept 10 per cent of the take, and where else in the world can you find a numbers game where the suckers get 90 per cent of their dough back?

Right after the *Okinawa* anchored and the crew was dismissed from quarters, heads began popping into Fatso's porthole and demanding dope on the winning number. Soon there was quite a crowd gathered outside.

"It ain't decided yet," yelled Fatso from his retreat. "I think the number is 25—but it won't be official till tomorrow morning. Now shove off you guys, and quit bothering me."

One George Washington Brown, steward's mate second class, stood rooted to the deck for a few seconds, his mouth ajar and his eyes bulging clear out of their sockets. Then he let out a whoop and hollered:

"That's *me* mistah Fatso. Lawsamercy that sho is mah number!" Whereupon George Washington Brown went galloping down the hangar deck toward the wardroom pantry flapping his arms and laughing like crazy.

Not long after this Commissar Jones hammered on the door of the incinerator compartment and yelled, "Hey, open up, Fatso, and let me in."

"Go peddle your papers," growled Fatso, who was not an admirer of the Commissar. "I'm cleaning up for Captain's inspection."

Commissar knew this was a lot of malarkey because Captain's Inspection was scheduled for the day after tomorrow and Fatso still had plenty of time. He replied "Okay wise guy. I just want to let you know I got the winning number this morning—28—do you want to pay me now or later?"

"Let's make it later pal," said Fatso. "You aren't even close by my watch."

Jones went away muttering to himself about that fat wop getting too big for his britches, and needing to be unshipped at the ankles and secured in the fore and aft position.

After Jones went away Fatso picked up his ship's telephone and dialled the number of the signal bridge.

"This is Gioninni down in the incinerator," he said.

"Hiya Fatso, what can I do for you? Send a signal to the Admiral?" came the cheerful reply from the bridge.

"Naw," said Fatso. "How's to look in the quartermaster's notebook and find out the time of anchoring for me?"

"It was close to 0926—I missed it a mile this time," replied the signal floozie.

"Tough luck, kid," said Fatso. "But look in the book, will you, and see what the official time was?"

A few minutes later the voice from the bridge said "The book ain't up here now. The navigator's yeoman came up and got it right after we anchored and he hasn't brought it back yet."

There was nothing irregular about that. The navigator's yeoman often has occasion to consult the quartermaster's rough notebook when he types the smooth log.

"Okay," said Fatso. "Gimme a call and let me know as soon as he brings it back."

Fatso then dialled the Chief Quartermaster in the chart house and said, "Say Chief, gimme a time check on your #1 chronometer for the anchoring pool, will ya?"

"Okay Fatso," said the Chief. "1058 coming up . . . ten seconds to go . . . five seconds . . . standby-y-y . . . MARK! 1058."

"Thanks," said Fatso. "I'm within 5 seconds of it. What time did you get for anchoring, chief?"

"I didn't get it exactly," replied the chief. "The Old Man brought her in like a bat out of hell this morning and he had us all sweating blood around here trying to keep up with him. But it was somewheres around 0925."

Just before noon the signal bridge rang back to Fatso and said "The Navigator's yeoman just brought the book back. Official

Now, Hear This!

time was 0928."

"Hunh?" said Fatso incredulously. "I don't think that's right."

"Well that's what the book says anyway. I gotta hang up now, the Dover just ran up our call flags."

Fatso began to smell a smell and it wasn't just the regular Naples smell. He locked up his shop and beat it up to the starboard gangway to see who was Officer of the Deck. Fatso had sufficient standing with most of the OOD's to ask for a careful check on the time of anchoring before they wrote up the log of the watch. But unfortunately the present OOD was not one of these. The Lieutenant was already writing up the watch when Fatso approached, saluted, and said

"Sir, can you tell me what time we anchored this morning. I gotta make a note in my incinerator log."

The Lieutenant, who wasn't as dumb as he looked, regarded Fatso skeptically. "Oh?" he said. "You gotta make a note . . . well anyway the time was 0928. I just logged it . . . there it is in the quartermaster's notebook."

"Sir," said Fatso, "I thought it was earlier than that. I . . . wonder, could there be a mistake?"

"I appreciate your interest in helping me to write up my log accurately," said the Lieutenant, "and anytime you need help running the incinerator just let me know. But I'll write my log without any help from you."

There was obviously no profit in beating along that tack any further so Fatso retired to the incinerator and sent out a call for an emergency meeting of all his cronies, who were also the Board of Trustees for the anchoring pool.

These men were the same Mark and Mod. of sailormen as Fatso. They were all career men with at least twelve years' service, but none allowed his career to interfere with his personal comfort or to infringe on his civil rights. Their outlook on the regulations was the same as Fatso's and in any nonregulation enterprise they were

28

as dependable as a dumb marine on sentry duty. They could give all outward appearances of obeying the regulations literally while at the same time committing offenses that can be severely punished under the Universal Code of Military Justice.

Enlisted men who possess the strength of character, initiative, and imagination to do this naturally gravitate into positions of responsibility and trust in any military organization. So it was with Fatso's cronies. His closest pals were Satchelaft Anderson, Beer Bottle Bates, and Scuttlebutt Grogan, three tried and true musketeers who had been through many hazardous adventures with Fatso. Fatso's cohorts between them had quite a collection of Navy Crosses, Silver and Bronze Stars, and other awards for heroism in battle during the war.

But being brave in battle didn't count much with Fatso. Everybody is supposed to do *that*. Keeping your nerve when the MP's or the cops closed in, standing by a shipmate in distress, or willingness to stick your neck out and break a few regulations for a worthy cause, those were the qualities that Fatso looked for in his pals. Satchelaft, Scuttlebutt, Beer Bottle and the rest of them had amply demonstrated these naval virtues many times over.

The happy band of brothers also included such characters as the Captain's and Exec's yeomen, the top sergeant of marines, the head cook in the galley, the boss yellow shirt on the flight deck, the coxswain of the Captain's gig and others of similar stature. They were actually the backbone of the U.S.S. *Okinawa* because, although they didn't actually run the ship themselves, they occupied positions from which they could influence the officers who did run it. Many a time they wangled officers into doing the right thing, and left the officers thinking that they (the officers) had figured the thing out for themselves. They could swing practically any deal on the ship, from providing a midnight banquet in Fatso's sanctum to chilling a bum rap at mast against a careless but well-meaning sailor.

Now, Hear This!

As each member of the gang arrived in the inner sanctum, Fatso supplied him with a can of beer. But when the Captain of the Paint Locker asked for Bourbon and water Fatso said "Nuts. You know the rules of this joint. No hard stuff till after working hours." When they had all assembled Fatso addressed the meeting as follows:

"Something stinks about the time of anchoring today. According to my watch we let go at 0925:18, give or take a few seconds. But the time that's going into the ship's log is 0928 and that's Commissar Jones' number . . . I dunno how he's doing this but I think he's trying to work a shenanigan. Now you guys get busy and find out what the dope is."

When Fatso's FBI went to work on solving a mystery on the U.S.S. *Okinawa* the contents of the latest "Top Secret Eyes Only" message from the CNO wasn't safe from scrutiny. While they were putting the suction on their pipelines and grilling various key sources Commissar Jones again appeared at the incinerator and said "How about it Fatso? I suppose you know by now that I hit the jackpot today. Are you ready to pay off now?"

"No," said Fatso slamming the lid down on his liquor locker and snapping the lock. "I hadn't heard about it yet. Must of been something wrong with my watch because I timed it at 0925 and my watch is usually pretty close to right."

"You pay off on the time in the smooth log don't you," asked Commissar innocently.

"Usually we do," conceded Fatso.

"Whaddayou mean *usually*," demanded Commissar.

"Well, I mean most of the time up to now we have," said Fatso . . .

"Well I'm telling you that I won that pot fair and square today," said Jones. "And I'm also telling you that if you try to gyp me out of it, you'll be making bad trouble for yourself." Jones looked right at the liquor chest as he said this.

"Okay pal," said Fatso. "If you had the right number you'll get the dough—if you didn't, you won't—and you can depend on that."

Late that afternoon the Board of Trustees assembled in the incinerator compartment again.

The Captain's yeoman reported first. "The time of anchoring in the smooth log will be 0928. That's the way it is in the quartermaster's notebook, the OOD's rough log, and that's the way it's being written up for the Captain's signature."

"Yabbut that ain't the time we anchored," said Satchelaft. "I checked the bell book in the engine room and that's more accurate than the quartermaster's log. They backed 2/3 at 0924-40 and backed full at 0925-15. The hook went down while they were spinning the throttles to back full and the winning number should be 25—I got 24 so I checked pretty accurately."

"I think I know what's behind this," said Scuttlebutt. "Commissar Jones put the navigator's yeoman on the report a couple of days ago and withdrew the report today. Jones says . . ."

"Never mind what Jones says," interrupted Fatso. "All we are interested in is the actual time of anchoring. I'm satisfied now and I'm ready to pay off to that mess boy on number 25. Do you guys go along with that?"

All around the circle the Trustees took grave swigs out of their beer cans and nodded their heads in agreement.

"There's going to be trouble about this," continued Fatso. "That guy Commissar Jones ain't going to like it. I don't know what he can do about it but don't any of you guys get mixed up in this. I'll paddle my own canoe with him."

There were graver swigs and more nods of agreement all around the circle.

Next day the Captain signed the official smooth log book with the time of anchoring recorded as 0928. Almost immediately Commissar Jones bounced into the incinerator compartment and de-

31

manded his 600 bucks.

Fatso looked steadily at Jones and said "Commissar, I'm sorry but there has been some mistake. The correct time of anchoring yesterday was 0925 even if the smooth log does say 0928. I paid off half an hour ago to Brown the Wardroom mess boy."

Commissar's face colored up with rage. "You are supposed to pay off on the time in the smooth log book."

"Most of the time we do," said Fatso patiently. "But sometimes there's a mistake and then we don't."

"Listen Wise Guy," stormed Commissar, "you're robbing me of 600 bucks, just the same as if you lifted it out of my locker. If you think you're going to get away with it—you're crazy."

Next morning Commissar Jones appeared in the Executive Officer's office just before Captain's inspection and turned in a report slip charging Fatso with having liquor in his possession aboard ship. This was a serious charge indeed because the U.S. Navy has been bone dry afloat since long before World War I. Even officers get a general court-martial for bringing liquor aboard, so it would be unthinkable to ignore such a charge against an enlisted man. Any petty officer convicted of having liquor aboard ship would certainly be busted, so when one petty officer puts another on the report for such a charge as this it usually indicates a deep-seated feud. The Commander's face assumed a stern set and he asked,

"You've got the evidence to back this up, have you?"

"Nossir. Not yet," said Jones. "But . . ."

The Commander's face relaxed and he demanded, "Then what's the idea of making a report like this one?"

"I know where he keeps it, sir, and I can take you to it any time, sir."

"Where does he keep it?"

"In the incinerator compartment, sir. He's got two cases of beer and about a dozen bottles of whiskey there right now, sir."

"That's impossible," said the Commander. "How could he hide

all that stuff when he has to have the place clean and opened up once a week for Captain's inspection?"

"He puts it inside that big furnace for Captain's inspection and piles a lot of rubbish in front of it so when you look in the furnace all you see is rubbish. Do you want me to take you there now, sir?"

"No," said the Commander. "It's just about time for inspection. We'll do it right after inspection and before the crew is dismissed from quarters."

Inspection was a few minutes late starting that morning. When the Commander went up to the cabin to inform the Captain that the men were all in ranks and ready, he asked to have a few words in private with him before the inspection started.

"It's about that guy Fatso Gioninni again, Captain," said the Commander.

"What now?" asked the Captain in a way that indicated he wouldn't be surprised no matter what.

"He's got a load of liquor down in the incinerator."

"Okay," said the Captain, "wait until tonight and then make him heave it overboard when nobody will see him."

"Too late for that, Captain. It's a matter of official record now. The Master At Arms put him on the report."

"That's bad," said the Captain. "There must be a grudge behind that—how are we going to handle this thing?"

"Of course," said the Commander, "if this report ever gets to you officially there's nothing you can do but give him a court-martial."

"All right then, don't let it get to me."

"But if I just pigeonhole it, the word will get all over the ship in nothing flat. In fact it will probably get over to the flagship too."

"So it would," agreed the Captain. "But you know just as well as you are standing there that neither of *us* is going to bust Fatso . . . so?"

"Well, sir," said the Commander, "no court would convict a

33

man on verbal evidence in a case like this. You've got to have the bottles sitting on the table in the court. We've got to get rid of the evidence without seeming to connive in it. I told the MAA I would go up to the incinerator compartment to get it right after inspection. If I go up there and there's no liquor there, then everything would look okay, wouldn't it?"

"Sure," said the Captain, "but you can't lug a lot of liquor out on the hangar deck and heave it overboard while an inspection is going on."

"No. But Captain, if you will inspect the incinerator this morning and will . . ." It took only a minute to convince the Captain that there was a sound solution to their dilemma, a solution that met the demands of naval justice, and at the same time satisfied the human obligations which sometimes complicate the administration of justice.

As soon as the Captain completed his inspection of the crew that morning he announced his intention of inspecting the hangar deck and in due course his party arrived at the incinerator. The compartment was shined up like a million bucks, the big furnace glistened with a new coat of black paint, and Fatso Gioninni attired in his best suit of dress blues beamed proudly.

"Your compartment looks very well, Gioninni," said the Captain after peering carefully into all corners, lockers and chests.

"Thank you, Captain," said Fatso with a grin.

"By the way Gioninni," said the Captain, "that's a pretty big furnace you've got there. Where does the air for it come from when the ship is battened down?"

"Oh this is a forced-draft furnace, Captain. That blower over there sucks in all the air we need from the flight deck and blows it right into the bottom of the furnace." Fatso pushed a button, the blower began to rumble, and you could hear the air whoosh through the furnace. "No trouble about air," said Fatso stopping the blower.

34

"Trash" Disposal Problem

"How long does it take to burn up one furnace full of rubbish?" asked the Captain.

"About 8 to 10 minutes, depending on just what kind of rubbish you've got in there," said Fatso.

"What kind you got in there now?" asked the Captain sociably as the other members of the party began to wonder about his sudden interest in trash disposal.

"Well," said Fatso, " . . . er . . . that is . . . it's really mostly wood, Cap'n—old crates and boxes and stuff like that there."

"I'd like to see how one of these furnaces operates," announced the Captain. "How about lighting it off for me right now?"

"I can't very well do that now, Cap'n," said Fatso in alarm.

"Why not," demanded the Captain.

"Because, well . . . because . . . that there blower got a bum bearing, Cap'n—I gotta change it first," said Fatso glibly.

The Captain punched the starter button and listened as the blower rumbled up to speed. Turning to the Chief Engineer, he said "How does she sound to you, Chief?"

The Chief listened professionally, put his hand on the blower casing to feel the vibration and said cautiously, "It *seems* to be running OK, Captain."

"Yabbut it always does just before it breaks down. Can I stop it now, Captain?" said Fatso desperately.

"No," said the Captain. "Light her off."

There was no use stalling around any further. Fatso borrowed a match from the Chief Master at Arms and ruefully applied it to the armful of excelsior that was stuffed under the grate bars. Soon a hot fire was roaring in the furnace. The Captain strode around the furnace inspecting it from all angles. He had Fatso point out and explain the damper control, and opened the peep hole in the front to look in at the dancing flames.

"How hot does it get in there Gioninni?" asked the Captain.

Now, Hear This!

"Pretty hot, Cap'n," said Fatso miserably. "Hot enough to melt tin cans."

"How about glass? Will it melt bottles?" asked the Captain innocently.

Fatso shot a shrewd look at the Captain's sober face and said "Yessir—plenty hot enough for that."

The Captain stalled around for about five minutes, puttering here and there, and asking more questions. He was just about to leave when there was a series of loud bangs from inside the furnace.

"Must be pretty knotty wood you've got in there," said the Captain.

"Yessir that's right. The wood they put in crates nowadays is awful stuff, sir," observed Fatso as another ripple of internal explosions added weight to this opinion. The furnace labored, panted, and backfired a couple of times while the whole inspecting party gaped and the Chief Engineer regretted that he had spoken so hastily about the bearing.

Soon after the inspection was over the Commander, who had not accompanied the Captain around the hangar deck, appeared in the cabin and reported: "I have just finished a thorough inspection of the incinerator, Cap'n and I'm glad to report there is no liquor there."

"Commander, I wish you could have been there," chuckled the Captain. "He must have had enough stuff in that furnace to stock the Army-Navy club bar. It sounded like 20-millimeter guns around Okinawa when those bottles started busting. I thought the Chief Engineer was going to swallow his false teeth."

"There's apt to be a bit of trouble on the hangar deck, Cap'n," observed the Commander.

"Might be . . . might be," said the Captain.

That afternoon the Commander passed Commissar Jones on the hangar deck and was not surprised to note he had a black eye almost as big as the starboard hawsepipe. The Commander sent his orderly to summon Fatso from the incinerator.

"What's the matter with your hand, Gioninni?" inquired the Commander with a sympathetic glance at the cast on Fatso's saluting hand.

"I busted it, sir, trying to explain something to a guy."

"All right now," said the Commander easing over to an isolated corner and motioning for Gioninni to follow. "Listen, Gioninni, you only saved *my* life once. I've saved that worthless hide of yours about a dozen times now."

"Yessir. Aye aye sir," said Fatso innocently.

"Now get this straight, Fatso. There's to be no more liquor aboard this ship. None whatever—understand?"

"Who, me, Commander, why I wouldn't never do nothing like that Sir."

"Okay. This is your last warning," said the Commander severely. "Next time you get out of line I'm going to lower the boom on you." The Commander screwed his face up into what he hoped was a fearsome scowl.

"Aye aye, Sir," said Fatso, with an impudent wink which the Commander pretended not to see.

⚓ CHAPTER TWO

Un-holy Smoke

"STAND by-y-y—EXECUTE!" barked the Staff Duty Officer on the Admiral's bridge of the *Okinawa*, acting Flagship of the Mediterranean Fleet. A new Admiral had just come aboard and the Fleet was engaged in tactical exercises with thirty ships, large and small, maneuvering at high speed in perfect formation like a well-drilled ballet troup in response to flag signals from the *Okinawa*.

On the signal bridge, at the command "EXECUTE," a seaman yanked a halyard and a gaily colored array of signal flags came fluttering down from the yardarm, thus touching off a 90-degree turn to starboard. Similar hoists of flags whipped down from yardarms throughout the fleet; chief signalmen barked at their sweating helpers to get the lead out of their ass and restow them flags, while helmsmen spun their wheels and thirty ships leaned into their turns leaving creamy curved wakes behind them, all in perfect geometric pattern astern.

The Admiral surveyed the scene with a critical eye and found it pretty good. He was about to say so to his Chief of Staff when a hapless little destroyer in the outer screen began spewing a cloud of black smoke from her after stack. This is a serious breach of

38

naval decorum at any time. To do it in the midst of fleet maneuvers is like emitting a sonorous belch at a formal banquet.

The Chief of Staff, an old destroyer man himself, shrugged his shoulders apologetically on behalf of the little ship, and the Admiral waited a decent interval of about half a minute before cracking her knuckles. Then he said, "Tell that destroyer to stop smoke."

The chief signalman, waiting expectantly at the Admiral's elbow, whirled and roared, "Outboard hoist—pennant two—pennant three, pennant zero . . . second hoist—XRAY—MABEL—BAKER—two-block 'em! Snap into it down there!"

Signal floosies leaped from one end of the flag bag to the other as if the Old Nick himself were prodding them, bending on each flag as the chief named it. Other sailors heaved around on the halyards dragging the flags out of the rack as quickly as they were made fast and hauling the humiliating signal up to the yardarm where not only destroyer number 230 but the whole fleet could see it.

The answering XRAY-MABEL-BAKER was flying from the blushing destroyer's yardarm almost before the flagship got it two-blocked, acknowledging that the signal was understood and would be complied with. But the offending smoke continued to pour in an ugly black cloud from the after stack.

After a minute of tense silence the Admiral snapped, "Give them the INTERROGATORY."

"Third hoist," yelled the chief, "What-the-hell flag."

A yellow flag with a black circle in the center shot up the yardarm, publicly indicating to all ships present the Admiral's disapprobation of the destroyer's lubberly conduct.

That night after taps Fatso's cronies gathered in the incinerator compartment for their usual evening snack of steak and eggs. The big furnace room was a sort of extraterritorial sanctum into which the long arm of naval discipline did not reach, and where taps and reveille were whenever Fatso decided to have them. Every night at sea right after the rest of the crew turned in, Fatso's cronies assembled there to discuss global strategy, partake of "leftover" food from the galley and hoist a nightcap or two.

This evening ship's cook "Bellyache" Barnes, seated on a bucket in front of the big trash furnace, was broiling a mess of tenderloin steaks left over from the crew's evening meal (which had been baked beans). Fatso and his cronies were reviewing events of the day as they awaited their steaks.

"This new Admiral is a holy terror," observed Jughead Smith, whose station was on the flag bridge. "Captains and Commanders don't mean *nothin'* to him—he's got all the skippers in this fleet jumping up and down like a bunch of trained monkeys."

"I been with him before," said Fatso. "He was Chief of Staff in the task group I was in at the end of the war. He isn't really a bad guy—but he used to keep that what-the-hell flag bent on and ready to hoist any time—it went up and down at the yardarm like a yo-yo all day long. He won't bother guys like us but I'm glad I'm not a four-stripe skipper in this Sixth Fleet now."

"Don't be too sure about that," said Beer Bottle Bates. "Maybe the old guy himself won't bother us, but some of the characters he brought aboard with this new staff, maybe they might."

"What can they do to *us?*" demanded Fatso.

"Well, for instance, he's got a greasy two-and-a-half-striper for Personnel Officer who must be striking for two stars. He goes snooping about the fleet sticking his nose into stuff that's none of his business . . ."

"I think I know him," said Fatso. "He must be the one who came down here last week with a bag full of confidential stuff from the code room to be burned . . . he didn't seem to be such a bad guy. He was kind of friendly and sociable in fact."

"Yeah?" said Beer Bottle, "the other day he found out the *Salem* was over her allowance on chief signalmen and he made them transfer old Grampaw Hogan to a destroyer."

"Old Grampaw?" said Fatso indignantly, "why a week on a tin can will kill that poor old guy. They had him in charge of the sail locker on the *Salem*, where he didn't have nothing to do except sew up signal flags."

"That's what this two-and-a-half-striper found out—and that's why he made them transfer Grampaw and put a seaman in his place."

"That's too bad," observed Fatso, "but poor old Hogan always was unlucky—remember that time in Panama, Beer Bottle, when the shore patrol raided Maime Kelley's, and all of us got away except Grampaw?"

Beer Bottle remembered. "Grampaw would have got away too," he observed, "except that dame we used to call the Screaming Beazel claimed he owed her ten bucks and wouldn't let him have his pants." Scuttlebutt and Fatso shook their heads sadly and took smug comfort in the fact that such things never happened to them.

But next day Fatso found out they could happen. The Executive Officer sent for him and was wearing a long face when Fatso appeared at his stateroom.

"Yes Sir," said Fatso, with only the merest trace of familiarity to show for their twenty years of firm friendship.

"Fatso," said the Commander, "this is going to be a bad shock to you . . . but I've got to put you to work."

"Well now Commander, you know I don't mind work," said Fatso tolerantly. "I'm always ready to do odd jobs."

"This is different, Fatso," said the Commander gravely. "You're being transferred to the flight deck . . . starting tomorrow, you'll be leading boatswain's mate of the A-1 Division."

"You mean—you mean I—lose my incinerator job?" asked Fatso incredulously.

"I'm sorry, but I do," said the Commander. "They've finally smoked you out of that cozy harbor," and he handed Fatso an order from the Admiral addressed to the Sixth Fleet.

41

Now, Hear This!

". . . It has come to my attention that petty officers in the fleet are not always being employed in the proper work corresponding to their specialized ratings. This is particularly true of older men, some of whom are doing jobs which could be done just as well by seamen. Commanding Officers are directed to scrutinize their billet assignments and correct such abuses wherever found."

Fatso scanned the order dubiously and then said, "But Commander, you don't think this applies to *me*—do you, sir?"

"I would never dream of reaching such a conclusion on my own hook," said the Commander. "But the matter has been taken out of my hands," and he handed Fatso a piece of paper headed:

"Memo from the Admiral."

It was addressed to the Commanding Officer, U.S.S. *Okinawa*, and its subject was "My recent order on proper employment of petty officers #15A/32-SS." It said, "Gioninni, BM1c on your ship, is a case in point. This man is now in charge of the incinerator, a billet which can be adequately filled by a new recruit." It was signed "by direction."

"Holy smokes," said Fatso, "I didn't think Admirals bothered about such things."

"They don't," said the Commander, "I doubt if the Admiral knows anything about this memo. It's from that little twerp of a Personnel Officer," he added bitterly. (Commanders don't usually refer to two-and-a-half-stripers as twerps when speaking to enlisted men, but in this case the Exec was burned up by the officious meddling in the internal administration of his ship.)

"But anyway," added the Commander, "We've got no choice in the matter now. Tomorrow you take over on the flight deck."

That evening there was an indignation meeting in the incinerator that bordered on being what a military lawyer would call a "mutinous assembly." After Fatso announced the shocking news that the incinerator club was about to be broken up there was a stunned

42

silence for a moment. Then Satchelaft suddenly blurted

"Why, that sonofabitch . . ."

"Don't blame the Commander," said Fatso. "It ain't his fault."

"Commissar Jones is the one I mean," declared Satchelaft. "This is one of his jobs."

"How do you figure that?" asked Fatso.

"Just a couple of days ago right after the Admiral put out that fleet order I seen Commissar suckin' up to that 2½-stripe personnel officer on the staff. They was down on the hangar deck. Commissar was talking real smooth to him, and pointing over here to the incinerator. I wondered at the time what the hell was cooking. Now I know. Commissar was putting the little bastard up to write that memo to the Exec about you, Fatso."

"By golly I think you're right," said Fatso. "The other day, when he came down here with that burn bag he was checking up on what Commissar had told him. He couldn't have found out any other way."

"We ought to put Commissar in a bag and stuff him in this here furnace," declared Scuttlebutt.

"If that 2½-striper ever comes snooping around the engine room I'm going to drop an 18-inch Stillson wrench on him," promised Satchelaft.

"There's no use beating your gums that way," said Fatso philosophically. "In this here Navy when they give you a bum deal there's only two things you can do. You can relax and enjoy it—or you can make them change it. I don't think I'd like it up on the flight deck," he added and relapsed into deep thought while the gripe session continued.

Now Fatso, in addition to being an expert hand at deck seamanship, was also an ingenious and resourceful man with considerable mechanical know-how. He had proved that a number of times when the U.S.S. *Enterprise* got hit by Jap bombs and damage-control parties had to think fast in the midst of smoke and flames.

In fact, many *Enterprise* sailors claimed it was Fatso's inspired handling of the valves in the conflagration station when the hangar deck was blazing all around him, that saved the Big E from destruction.

After a few minutes' silence a gleam came into Fatso's eyes. Wheels began grinding inside his shrewd head and finally he said

"Hey Scuttlebutt . . . what do you engineers do when the bridge wants you to make a smoke screen?"

"We squirt a stream of fuel oil about the size of your little finger into the flue gases just above the boilers," said Scuttlebutt. "Partial combustion of the raw oil makes heavy black smoke come out of the stack."

"It sure does," said Fatso. "You know, that new guy takes over the incinerator tomorrow morning . . . I wonder how long he'd last in this job if he made a couple of smoke screens at the wrong time."

Nobody could fathom what Fatso might have in mind, but they all knew he didn't indulge in idle speculation on important matters of this kind. They waited respectfully and expectantly for enlightenment.

"Suppose," said Fatso, "we could squirt fuel oil into the flue of this here trash furnace every now and then . . . that would make a smoke screen, wouldn't it?"

"Yeah," said Scuttlebutt admiringly. "All we gotta do is lead a quarter-inch tube into his uptakes and connect it to one of the galley fuel-oil lines just outside of here."

"It's not quite that simple," said Fatso. "You can't have oil squirting in there all the time. This furnace is only lit off a couple of times a day. You only want the oil when he starts the furnace and only for a little while."

"Yabbut we can't very well have somebody peeking in here all day long to see when he lights off," objected Scuttlebutt.

"That's right," said Fatso. "But, why can't we fix it so that when-

44

ever he does light off, he will start the oil going himself?"

"How you gonna do that?" asked Scuttlebutt eagerly.

"This furnace works by forced draft," said Fatso. "That big blower over there in the corner forces air into the fire box and blows the smoke up the stack. Whenever you burn trash that blower is running. Now, if we had a little electric oil pump connected to this quarter-inch line we're going to rig, we could hook the motor up to the starting panel of that there blower. Then, whenever he started the blower he would start the pump too."

Unconcealed hero worship shone from the faces of all of Fatso's cronies.

"Yabbut where are you going to get this oil pump?" demanded Scuttlebutt.

"We don't need a very big one," said Fatso. "These new jet planes we got now have a small electric fuel-transfer pump in them. Now if we could get one of those . . ."

"I'll get you one," said Satchelaft eagerly. "I helped salvage that jet that got creamed yesterday. She's a major overhaul job and so she'll be a hangar-deck lily for the rest of the cruise. I'll get the fuel-transfer pump out of that one."

"What are we waiting for?" asked Fatso. "We gotta get this job done tonight."

In the next three hours eager hands made expert work of reducing Fatso's conception to practice. They installed a five-gallon fuel-oil tank in an inconspicuous place in the uptakes outside the incinerator compartment. They connected a quarter-inch copper tube from this tank to the fuel pump from the crashed plane, and led the discharge side of the line into the flue of the trash furnace. Wires were run from the starting panel of the blower motor to the fuel-pump motor and one wire, with a cut-out switch, was run up to the flight deck. This cut-out switch would enable an observer on the flight deck—where Fatso would be stationed beginning tomorrow—to stop the little pump when and if he thought it had gone far enough.

When the gang reassembled in the incinerator room for a final round of coffee after completing the job, Scuttlebutt said:

"You know—I hate to think what's going to happen to our Skipper when this thing cuts loose—too bad we have to do it to such a nice guy."

"Yeah," said Fatso, "and you can bet your flat-hat it won't stop with the skipper. This whole ship will be red hot for a couple of days until they get somebody back down here who knows how to run this furnace right."

Anyone who has been in a military organization when the heat is applied to the top man will appreciate the soundness of this last observation. On that note of wisdom the meeting adjourned.

Bright and early next morning seaman Willie Keeler reported at the incinerator to relieve Fatso of command. Willie was a nice clean-cut lad who learned quickly and Fatso couldn't help liking the cut of his jib. Fatso gave him a thorough briefing on the S.O.P. of the incinerator. He explained the starting panel to Willie and showed him how to vary the speed of the blower depending on how big a load of stuff he had in the furnace. He warned him not to accept trash with any glass or scrap metal in it, and to save any oily stuff to burn after dark when a little smoke wouldn't matter. He told him almost all he knew about operating a trash furnace, and Willie absorbed it very quickly.

"Good luck to you, Willie," said Fatso as he shoved off to take over his new duties up on the flight deck. "Good luck to you too, Fatso," replied Willie.

The fleet's tactical maneuvering exercises that morning were rather special. Two British cruisers and a division of Italian destroyers had joined the task group during the night, so naturally all nationalities were on their mettle to do things perfectly this morning. The exercises started with simple maneuvers to give the newcomers a chance to get the feel of things, and worked up gradually to the more complicated ones. For the first couple of hours everything went well, and the Admiral found nothing to criticize.

Meantime, compartment cleaners from all over the ship appeared at the incinerator and deposited the trash which they had harvested in their morning's work. Willie puttered around the furnace room humming happily while he shined bright work and generally tidied things up. By eleven o'clock a good-sized pile of trash had accumulated, and Willie began loading it into the furnace to burn.

At this time the Fleet was performing the rather intricate maneuver of rotating the Fleet axis 120 degrees. The flagship was the pivot point for this evolution, in which all ships assume new stations with respect to the guide. Ships were steaming in all directions at once, some maneuvering to increase distance, some to lose it, and others simply changing bearing. Smack in the middle of this evolution Willie Keeler lit off his trash furnace and the *Okinawa* began belching a great cloud of black smoke.

Her own bridge personnel saw it first. The Officer of the Deck leaped to the squawk box and barked at the engine room "STOP SMOKE." Seconds later, the Admiral, on the level just below the bridge happened to glance aloft. "Good God!" he said.

By this time everybody on the bridge was jumping up and down, pointing to the stack and yelling "STOP SMOKE." The Captain grabbed the direct phone to the engine room and called for the Officer of the Watch. "What the hell's the matter," he demanded. "You're making a regular smoke screen."

A peremptory command had already gone out from the engine room to all fire rooms, and the water tenders were peering through peepholes in the boiler casings at the stack gases of their particular boilers to make sure they were not the offenders. Soon the various fire rooms were happily reporting, "Number 2, clear stack . . . Number 4, clear stack . . ." and so on through all eight steaming boilers.

The officer of the engine room watch flipped the bridge switch

47

on his squawk box and reported somewhat smugly, "Smoke is stopped, sir." The blast from the bridge in reply to this outrageous statement nearly caused first-degree burns for all engineers on watch in the control room, because by now the cloud of smoke pouring from the *Okinawa's* stack was assuming monstrous proportions.

The Admiral made a heroic effort to keep himself under control, but each succeeding billow of smoke that rose from the stack brought the breaking point closer. An Admiral, although physically on board his Flagship, is supposed to deal with her in a detached and impersonal manner the same as any other ship in his fleet. But most Admirals favor her a little bit, and instead of hoisting a rude signal addressed to the Flagship for the whole fleet to see, will usually correct her mistakes by direct informal action. But by the same token the Flagship should be a paragon of naval virtues, setting the example for the rest of the fleet to follow.

Finally the Admiral leaned out over the rail of the flag bridge and bellowed at the navigating bridge above, "CAPTAIN, STOP THAT SMOKE."

The Captain's head popped out on the level above, said "Aye, aye sir. Right away sir." And popped out of sight again.

Squawk boxes all over the ship blared forth, "Now the Chief Engineer report to the Captain on the bridge IMMEDIATELY."

All this yelling and excitement on the bridge distracted the attention of the helmsman and the OOD. They, as well as everyone else, were craning their necks aft hypnotized by the unthinkable public nuisance which the Flagship was committing. Just before the smoke started, the helmsman had put on ten degrees of right rudder to correct a small deviation from course to the left. In the ensuing uproar he had forgotten it! By now the *Okinawa* was ten degrees off course to the right and was rapidly picking up momentum in her swing. Fatso, observing from the flight deck, snapped the cut-out switch on the fuel oil pump and stopped the smoke at this point, just as the Captain, Navigator and OOD all detected

48

the helmsman's error and exploded simultaneously.

Let us draw the veil of charity over the next five minutes on the *Okinawa's* bridge. Suffice to say that before they got the snafu straightened out and resumed proper position in the formation, the Admiral had the yardarm full of signals addressed to the *Okinawa* including XRAY-MIKE-BAKER, INTERROGATORY— and (crowning insult of all for a flagship) even the POSITION PENNANT.

Throughout all this Willie Keeler sang happily to himself down in the incinerator room as he heaved the trash into his furnace utterly oblivious of the havoc he wrought.

When the Chief Engineer arrived on the bridge all out of breath, the Flagship was almost back in position but the Captain's safety valve was still stuck wide open.

"Cap'n," he gasped, "every one of my water tenders reports he had a clear stack and—"

"Well then will you please tell me where in the *!!?* that thing back there came from," demanded the Captain pointing to what looked like a cloud from an atomic explosion about half a mile astern.

"I'm not trying to alibi, Cap'n," said the Chief, "but sometimes a little piece of grit gets stuck in a burner tip and causes a thing like that until it gets loose . . ."

"And if that's what happened then one of those water tenders of yours is lying. Now Chief, I don't want to be unreasonable, but I want it clearly understood . . . etc., etc."

Throughout the early afternoon Willie Keeler busied himself down in the incinerator painting some out-of-the-way corners which Fatso had neglected, and scraping the paint off several pieces of bright work which Fatso had covered over to save himself elbow grease when shining up for inspection. By three o'clock a pile of boxes and crates from the galley had accumulated outside the incinerator. Willie busted them up, loaded them into his furnace and lit her off.

This touched off almost an exact duplicate of the morning's disastrophy, except that this time the helmsman didn't dope off. When the squawk boxes again blared their demand for the Chief Engineer to report on the bridge they said, "ON THE DOUBLE." This is an unprecedented summons for a commissioned officer, especially a rather portly Commander.

This time the Chief had better sense than to open his mouth except to say, "Aye aye sir."

The Captain began by stating profanely and emphatically that this business had to stop. The Chief Engineer had already let word to that effect leak out to the fire-room personnel in even more emphatic terms than those used by the Captain. The Captain then made some derogatory remarks about engineers in general which the Chief didn't exactly go along with but was in no position at that moment to dispute. The Old Man announced that he was restricting the liberty of the entire engineers force until the Chief could produce the offenders responsible. He concluded his tirade with ". . . and starting right now I want a continuous watch to be stood by your engineer officers up in the foretop where they can look down the stack and see where that smoke is coming from."

"Aye aye sir," said the Chief and got the hell off that bridge.

(For the benefit of non-naval readers it must be explained that the big stack on a carrier is divided by athwartship bulkheads running clear up to the top, into three separate flues, each of which handles the stack gases from one of the three fire rooms.)

Next morning there was an air of expectant tenseness throughout the ship. When the Captain is off on a rampage word gets around fast and all hands stay out of sight as much as possible. Everyone knew that one more smoke screen would cause an upheaval and nobody wants to be near ground zero when a four-stripe Captain blows up.

Sure enough, about ten o'clock that morning Willie lit off the

incinerator, the faithful little pump did its stuff, and the atomic
blast occurred. But as pandemonium broke loose on the bridge,
the engineer Lieutenant up in the foretop began yelling, "IT'S
THE INCINERATOR—IT'S *NOT* THE ENGINEERS—THE
INCINERATOR!"

The Captain grabbed a megaphone and yelled aloft, "Are you
crazy? No incinerator ever put out that much—"

"It *is* the incinerator Cap'n. All the smoke is coming out of number one flue and all the boilers in number one fire room are *dead*."

Before the Captain could say a word the Exec and the OOD
were already trying frantically to get word down to the incinerator.
But the incinerator is not on any of the emergency battle circuits
and has no means of rapid communication with the bridge—except perhaps for one-way transmissions by smoke signal. The Junior Officer of the Deck went bounding down the ladders three steps
at a time to carry the word below in person.

But it's a long way down to the incinerator and before he got
there, the Commander thought of a quicker way. He called Central
Station and yelled, "Pull all power to the incinerator—cut 'em out
immediately." Central Station complied promptly pulling the
switches that supplied juice to the incinerator and, of course, the
great cloud of smoke coming out of the *Okinawa's* stack stopped
forthwith.

But by this time there was a roaring fire of dry wood going in
Willie's furnace. You can stop a blower and thus stop forcing the
products of combustion through the narrow flue and up the stack.
But you can't just snuff out *that* kind of fire by pulling a switch
. . . and the products of combustion have to go somewhere. They
began pouring out into the incinerator compartment.

The last few shots of oil which Fatso's little pump had squirted
into the flue while coasting to a stop ran down on top of the fire,
causing the furnace to burp, backfire, and blow the door open. The
dense black smoke which had been going up the stack to pollute

the Mediterranean sky came pouring out into the furnace room on the starboard side of the hangar deck.

Seconds later the man on watch in the hangar-deck conflagration station saw heavy black smoke surging into the hangar from below his cubbyhole. When fire breaks out on the hangar deck of an air-craft carrier you act first and conduct formal investigations later. . . . The watch pulled the fire alarm with one hand and the hangar-deck sprinkler system with the other.

General alarm bells clanged, bugles blew, and the dread word rang out on the public announcing system, "FIRE ON THE HANGAR DECK." Everyone on the ship dropped whatever they were doing and rushed to their assigned fire stations, closing water-tight doors, battening down hatches and leading out fire hoses.

For the Navy which fought and licked the great fires that almost destroyed the carriers *Essex, Bonne Homme Richard,* and *Franklin* during World War II, putting out an incinerator fire is child's play. The hangar-deck fire party arrayed in smoke helmets and asbestos suits floundered through the deluge from the sprinkler system and burst into the incinerator compartment dragging their hoses behind them. In a matter of seconds they drowned the blaze out and two fire-fighters emerged into the hangar leading Willie Keeler between them—coal-black from head to foot except for the whites of his eyes. True to the best traditions of the U.S. Navy, Willie had stuck to his post throughout the holocaust, struggling to reset his dead circuit breakers, re-energize his panel, and get his blower going again.

As soon as the fire was out the Captain came hurrying down the ladder to the flag bridge in response to a peremptory summons from the Admiral.

"Yessir," said the Captain banging his heels together and cracking up with a salute like a Marine on main gate sentry duty.

"My good man," said the Admiral, "I want it clearly understood that I've had enough of this." There followed a few statements which cannot be repeated in a book of this kind, tersely summarizing matters which the reader is already aware of. The Admiral continued ". . . one more exhibition like this and there is going to be a new Engineering Officer on this ship, to say nothing of a new Captain."

"Aye aye sir," said the Captain. "It won't happen again sir. We've found out what's been causing it."

"Well by the Great Horn Spoon, I'd say it's about time!" snorted the Admiral.

"It was a new, inexperienced incinerator man who . . ."

This was the wrong thing to say. "Do you mean to stand there and tell me," roared the Admiral, "that the reason why I've been humiliated and the U.S. Navy has been made ridiculous before a bunch of foreigners is that you picked a time like this to conduct kindergarten classes?"

"But Admiral," protested the Captain, "we've got a good experienced man for that job but—"

"But HORSEFEATHERS," snapped the Admiral—or words to that general effect, "I want you to put the best man you've got on that job and keep him there as long as my flag is flying in this ship."

"Aye aye sir," said the Captain, and took his departure at a rate of knots similar to that used by the Chief Engineer in leaving the bridge the day before.

That very afternoon Fatso returned the muster books for the A-1 Division to the boatswain's mate who had previously been their custodian on the flight deck, moved his gear back down to the incinerator and began cleaning up the mess. That evening Fatso and his cronies met as of old in the incinerator for their late repast, except that there was one new face in the circle. Willie Keeler was seated on a bucket near the furnace, all cleaned up by now and none the worse for his morning's adventures.

". . . like I told you son," Fatso was saying, "there's quite an

53

art to regulating this here furnace. You gotta watch the draft like a hawk and vary the speed of the blower depending on what kind of stuff you're burning. But don't be discouraged about losing this job —you've got lots of time ahead of you in this Navy, and you've got good stuff in you."

"What I can't understand," said Willie, "is how plain dry wood could possibly make all the smoke they *claim* it did."

"Don't cook that steak of Willie's too much," said Fatso to Bellyache Barnes, who was presiding over the cooking. "A young man like Willie needs his meat rare."

⚓ CHAPTER THREE

The Sea Bat

ONE AFTERNOON at sea, Fatso sat in his sanctum, his feet cocked up on the bulkhead, puffing a big cigar while Tony Kane, an aviation machinist's mate, fed trash into the blazing furnace. Tony, although only a third-class, was a jet plane captain, and since he was all caught up with his work on the plane, had come down this afternoon to help Fatso.

Fatso had no official striker assigned to him, but he never did any manual labor around the incinerator himself. Scores of eager young sailors like Tony were always glad to lend a hand at the trash furnace while Fatso sat back and regaled them with improbable tales of life on the *Enterprise* during the war.

Every day at least a dozen lads bringing buckets of trash from all parts of the ship would ask him, "Need any help today, Fatso?" The lucky one to whom he said "Yes" would spend the next couple of hours loading the day's trash into the furnace and listening to Fatso hold forth on how life in the new Navy wasn't what it used to be in the old days. The fact that it never had been either didn't cramp Fatso's style in telling about it.

Today he was just finishing one of his tales about how the *Enter-*

55

prise had won the war almost single handed ". . . and at the end of the battle, the Pacific Ocean around the Big E had blood guts and feathers from Jap Zeros all over it. So the Cap'n says to Bull Halsey, 'We got 'em all, Admiral,' and the Admiral says 'What took you so long this time Cap'n?' "

"Gee," said Tony, "how does it feel to be fighting battles like that every day? Don't you get the jumping jitters after a while?"

"Naw," said Fatso, "you get used to it after the first couple of years. And we used to take in a lot of slack between battles. There was something going on every minute of the day on that ship," he added reminiscently. "By the way son, didja ever see a sea bat?"

"A sea bat? No—what is it?"

"It's a strange little animal we used to catch on the *Enterprise*," said Fatso. "I ain't ever seen one on this bucket yet. But I'll bet maybe you could catch one on the hangar deck some night if you went about it right."

"Whaddaya hafta do?" asked Tony eagerly.

"Well son," said Fatso, "first you get a small cardboard box and cut holes in the side. Then . . ."

A few minutes later, when Fatso finished explaining, Tony was chuckling gleefully, and unashamed hero worship shone from his eyes. "Boy-oh-boy," he said, "I'm going to have me a sea bat by tomorrow morning."

That evening in the incinerator compartment a gripe session was in progress. "This navy is going to hell," announced Beer Bottle.

This, of course, is a proposition on which old timers have agreed ever since we've had a Navy.

"What is it now?" asked Fatso.

"Everything is getting mechanized now," said Beer Bottle. "They just finished installing a new computer in CIC today. It's a big box full of mechanical brains that knows all the answers—if you feed the right dope into it to begin with. This damn thing is supposed to know more about running a CIC than I do after twenty years' experience at it. Pretty soon we'll do everything with push-buttons and computers and they won't have any more use for old-timers like us."

"Don't worry about that, Beer Bottle," said Fatso. "They'll always need real sailormen as long as the ocean is made out of salt water."

"I dunno," objected Satchelaft, "it's the same way down in the engine rooms and fire rooms too. When I was on the FDR I could handle that 200,000-horsepower plant like it was a teakettle. I could find every valve switch and control lever in the dark and handle any casualty you can name except maybe a busted main shaft. But on here you just sit in an air-conditioned control booth and punch a lot of buttons that do all the thinking for you. All it takes to do it is a guy wearing glasses who hasn't had a haircut in a couple of months. They don't need me at all any more except to see that the place gets shined up good for inspection."

"Don't kid yourself," said Fatso. "When the shooting starts and some of this fancy automatic stuff gets busted they'll still have use for guys like us. And these new kids we're getting now aren't so different from what we used to be either."

"The hell they're not," said Satchelaft. "Those guys we got on here in training for the atomic carrier they're building go around all day with an armful of library books and they don't even know port from starboard. Maybe they know all about the Einstein theory but they can just barely find their way from the chow line to the head."

"They're not as different from us as you think," persisted Fatso. "Do you remember that sea-bat gag we used to pull back in the old days? I'll betcha it will still work on these guys."

Everybody knew about the sea-bat gag of course, but they all doubted it would work on present-day sailors.

"These guys are too smart for that," said Satchelaft. "And besides they're not even curious about what goes on around them unless there's a lot of vacuum tubes and transistors mixed up in it."

"I'd like to lay you a bet of ten bucks even money I can rope in half a dozen guys on that gag by 8 bells tomorrow morning," said Fatso.

"It's a bet," said Satchelaft.

Twenty minutes before flight operations were slated to begin next morning, Tony and two of his buddies appeared on the flight deck carrying brooms and a cardboard box which Tony set carefully down on the deck. It was about the size of a shoebox and had many small holes in the sides and top. Tony pulled a straw from his broom and all three sailors got down on their hands and knees peering into the holes while Tony poked inside the box with the straw. Leaning against the island and apparently paying no attention were Fatso, Beer Bottle, and Satchelaft.

Soon the boys around the box let out a whoop and Tony yelled, "Boy did you see that?" Then he stuck his finger gingerly into one of the holes, wiggled it around a bit and suddenly yanked it out yelling, "Yowie—he almost got me that time."

His two companions like to died laughing at this narrow escape. But almost immediately the three of them were peering into the holes again.

You can attract a curious crowd on the flight deck of a big aircraft carrier almost as easily as you can do it on Broadway by just standing in the middle of the sidewalk and looking up. Soon a couple of red-jerseyed fire-fighters noticed the commotion around the box and strolled over to see what was going on. Tony and his pals were too busy to pay any attention to them and continued poking around with the straw.

Finally one of the newcomers said, "Whatcha got in the box sailor?"

"A sea bat," said Tony, carefully probing with his straw while one of his companions squinted through the hole and said, "He's

58

way over in the far corner."

The fire-fighter had never heard of a sea bat before, but not wishing to betray his ignorance, he inquired.

"Where'dja get him?"

"Down on the hangar deck," said Tony. "The little son-of-a-gun was hanging from the tail of one of the jet airplanes . . ." then, as one of his buddies began lifting a corner of the box top he yelled, "Hey, don't let him out!"

"Lemme take a look, will ya, kid?" asked the fire-fighter.

"Sure, go ahead," said Tony giving up his place at the box and getting up on his feet. As the red shirt got down on his hands and knees and put one eye to a hole, Tony took a firm grip on his broom way down at the end of the handle. Then he wound up and cut loose with a swing that was reminiscent of Babe Ruth, catching the unsuspecting fire-fighter smack in the francis with a wallop that almost lifted him over the side.

The red shirt's reaction to this development was expressed in a series of unprintable comments climaxed by a direct threat to wreak serious bodily harm upon Tony. However, he soon realized that he would be outnumbered three to one in any such endeavor, and that he could avenge his wounded pride by simply sticking around a few minutes and encouraging other prospective victims to get caught.

Although there were many sailors puttering around on deck waiting for flight quarters to be sounded, only three or four had actually witnessed this episode. They immediately dropped what they were doing and hastily gathered around to assist Tony in this very worthy project.

Within the next ten minutes a dozen or so curious sailors had noticed the crowd and wandered over, had peeked into the box and gotten a hell of a big bang out of it. The box was now surrounded by a ring of sailors, including Fatso, which completely obscured what was going on at the box from newcomers who came out on deck. This crowd in the middle of the deck had, of course, an irresistible attraction for new arrivals.

At this point Lieutenant Commander T. Tuttle-Taylor, Legal Officer of the *Okinawa,* strolled out on deck with his hands in his pockets and his pockets in his pants. Hearing a hilarious howl go up from the crowd, he ambled over and elbowed his way into the center of the ring just too late to see another sailor learn some of the facts of life about nautical zoology.

Tony was standing with his back to the box laughing fit to bust and lapping up the enthusiastic applause of the crowd for his last wallop.

Lieutenant Commander T. Tuttle-Taylor fixed his eye on one of Tony's confederates, and said, "What you got in that box, son?"

The lad's eyes almost popped out of his head, he swallowed his gum and hastily said, "Er . . . nothing, sir."

"What do you mean—nothing," demanded Lieutenant Commander T. Tuttle-Taylor, bristling up and putting on his official manner.

"Well—I mean—that is—*nothing,* Sir," reiterated the sailor.

The Commander became somewhat belligerent, "I ast you, what have you got in the box," he said.

While the kid was racking his brains to find some better way of describing the contents of the box, Fatso's voice from the rear of the crowd said, "It's a sea bat, Commander."

"Oh! A sea bat," said the Legal Officer. "I'd like to see one of them," and so saying he stepped up to the box, stooped over and placed his eye near one of the holes.

All this time Tony had been so snowed under by the noisy hero worship of the crowd that he hadn't seen what was going on behind his back. When the crowd suddenly began making gestures indicating that another victim was all set up and waiting, he wasted no time in any searching investigations. He took a quick sight over his shoulder at the broad fanny sticking up near the box and uncorked the mightiest blow that had been struck all morning.

Men who work on a flight deck where danger is ever present, take cover instantly and instinctively when disaster strikes. Before the Legal Officer could straighten up and whirl around, the crowd had scattered like a covey of quail, leaving Tony rooted to the spot with the broom in his hands, goggling at the irate Lieutenant Commander.

Lieutenant Commander T. Tuttle-Taylor was not the kind of an officer that sailors can clout in the ass with a broom promiscuously. All in one breath he demanded Tony's name, rate and division, and informed him he was on the report. While Tony was still trying to gather his scattered wits and explain his informal treatment of the Commander, bugles, bells, and squawk boxes blared forth the call to flight quarters and Tony had to drop discussion of his personal problems and hurry to his official business.

He double-timed to the Banshee jet fighter parked at the head of the air group on deck, cast off the wing lines, and climbed into the cockpit to check that everything was ready for starting the engines when the pilots came on deck. This was the squadron commander's plane—or rather, the squadron commander flew it. But actually, of course, it was Tony's plane. He was the plane captain, who certainly has at least as much claim on a plane as the pilot does. He was responsible for keeping this plane in flying condition, and for correcting the squawks entered on the yellow sheet by the pilot. He knew every nut, bolt, safety wire and zerk fitting in its fuselage, and he groomed that plane for each flight as if it were Man-O'-War on the day of the Derby.

Soon the pilots came dog-trotting up from the ready rooms and Tony helped Commander Cue into the cockpit, adjusted his parachute harness, and tightened up his shoulder straps. "She's all set to go, Cap'n," said Tony. "I fixed the aileron boost valve—and the fuel-transfer pump is working OK now."

As the squadron commander nodded his approval, Tony jumped

off the wing and took station out in front of the plane to wait for the starting ritual. In a few minutes word boomed out over the flight deck bull horns.

"Now check all loose gear about the decks . . ."

Tony scanned the deck around his plane to make sure there were no cockpit covers, monkey wrenches, brooms, or sea-bat boxes lying around adrift to be sucked up into the engine intake.

"Check wheel chocks and wing lines . . ." chanted the master of ceremonies on the bridge. Blue, red, and green-shirted sailors in the deck crew made their final inspections of these items and held their fists out with thumbs up.

"Check propeller clearance. . . ." Tony had no propellers to check on his plane but he made sure his air scoops were open.

"Stand clear of propellers . . ." Tony instinctively looked behind and on both sides because you only get to make one mistake about propellers.

"START ENGINES . . ." Boomed the bull horns.

The whine of starters was followed by a few sporadic coughs and then the whole flight deck burst into the thunderous symphony of powerful engines. Tony ducked under the nose of the plane and held on to a wheel strut, listening approvingly while the jets snarled up to half power and then down to idling speed again. When the yellow-shirted taxi director held both his arms over his head with fists clenched, Tony noted the brake bands grabbing the wheels as Commander Cue stepped on the rudder pedals. The taxi director dropped his arms and made sweeping motions telling Tony to jerk the wheel chocks loose and scramble out from under there, while the plane rolled forward toward the catapult.

Tony's job was done now, so bracing himself against the 40 knots of wind across the deck and the hot blast of jet exhausts, he scurried expertly through the maze of whirling propellers over to the edge of the deck. Dropping into the gallery walkway he ran forward to the bow to watch his baby go off.

The Sea Bat

As Commander Cue taxied into position, the catapult gang swarmed around him. A catapult crew works with split-second precision like a troupe of acrobats, and in less time than it takes to tell about it, they had double-checked a dozen vital items, had hooked on the bridle and tail fitting, and had tensioned the catapult for the shot. A yellow shirt standing with his arms tightly hugging his chest suddenly shot both arms out horizontal and the wings of the Banshee swung down from the folded to the spread position. One green-shirt on each side watched until the red locking pin on his wing disappeared into the locked position, stuck out his fist with the thumb-up signal, and ducked out of the way. The yellow-shirt pointed to the catapult officer with both hands and as Commander Cue nodded "Roger," ran aft to start bringing the next plane up to the catapult. In a few more seconds Tony's plane would be hurled into the air at 100 knots from a standing start.

The catapult officer raised his right arm with two fingers extended, beat the air with a final turn-up signal, and the jets roared up to full gun. Then Tony's blood ran cold as he saw the red locking pin on the port wing pop out to the unlocked position. A catapult shot in that condition meant instant and certain disaster.

There is no use trying to yell a warning over the full-throated roar of engines on a flight deck. Commander Cue was already giving the salute signal meaning "all set to go." All hands were on their marks like a football team on the line of scrimmage and the catapult officer was about to snap his arm down in the signal that would be relayed down to the bowels of the ship telling the crew of the giant catapult engine to fire.

There was only one chance of stopping that shot now and Tony took it. He vaulted up out of the catwalk and straddled the catapult track with his arms extended. If they fired now it would be the end of him, as well as his plane and his squadron commander.

Some catapult officers fire instantly on the pilot's salute signal. Good ones automatically shoot a quick glance down the track be-

63

fore snapping their arms down. The one on the *Okinawa* was a good one and he saw Tony just in time to freeze his arm in the vertical position, holding the shot. It was a touch-and-go proposition but none of the crew on deck or below jumped the gun or got off side. Keeping his right arm frozen aloft, the catapult officer reached up with his left hand, wrapped his fist around the two extended fingers and slowly pulled his arm down, shaking his head emphatically from side to side as he did so.

Down in the bowels of the ship the tense crew on the catapult engine relaxed as the yellow stand-by light went back to red instead of green. The chief in charge growled "That would have been a perfect shot—all pressures and clearances exactly right—why can't those monkeys on deck make up their minds?"

It took only a few seconds to relock and double-check the wings on Commander Cue's plane. In due course he was fired off, and the rest of the deck load launch proceeded without further incident.

While this little drama was being enacted on deck, Lieutenant Commander T. Tuttle-Taylor was down below in his office thumbing through his military law books. The Commander didn't know too much about military law, and knew even less about the Navy. He was one of the benefits bestowed upon the Navy by a grateful Congress at the end of World War II.

Right after the war, Congress in its wisdom had decided that maybe wars would be won faster if they were fought in a more legal manner and if lawyers had more to say about global strategy. So they enacted a law tearing down the time-honored codes of military justice in the Army and Navy and erecting a new edifice known as the Uniform Code of Military Justice.

This code is a Philadelphia lawyer's dream and makes the administration of military justice so complicated that it was necessary to create thousands of additional billets for lawyers in the Army,

Navy, and Air Force. These billets provide soft jobs for some barristers who couldn't make a living on the outside and at the same time create more elbow room for the civilian mouthpieces, so the lawyers gained on all fronts.

Lieutenant Commander T. Tuttle-Taylor was the legal beagle assigned in accordance with the new code to the *Okinawa*. He had had two years of war experience in the Navy, as yeoman-in-charge of the library at Norman, Oklahoma, and after the war, under the GI Bill of Rights, had attended a college where his uncle was a professor and received a certificate saying he was a lawyer. When the Navy, looking for men with both legal and Naval training to fill the new billets, had offered him a commission, he immediately chucked up his job as a plumber's helper and accepted it.

The only fly in the Lieutenant Commander's ointment now, outside of an acute pain in the seat of his pants, was that the reforming lawyers had rigged the new code so that it was almost impossible to convict anybody of anything except piracy on the high seas or possibly an aggravated case of treason. They had fixed it so that it's easy to get away with first-degree murder—if you are properly advised by legal experts.

Commander T. Tuttle-Taylor didn't want to pin a murder rap on Tony, but he did feel that the very least he could settle for was the charge of "Wantonly assaulting his superior officer." Of course, theoretically, the new code is supposed to protect sailors from just this sort of business, but actually you can never devise any code that will protect its beneficiaries from peculiar individuals charged with administration of the code. In this case the Commander didn't take long to figure out how he could lower the boom on Tony more effectively than it could ever have been done under the old code.

He designated his own assistant, Ensign Dibble, to be Tony's legal adviser, and made it quite plain to the Ensign that he would tolerate no legal pettifoggery. He instructed Dibble to warn Tony about the danger of incriminating himself by answering questions.

65

Now, Hear This!

He said, "This is an open-and-shut case. It is your duty as his legal adviser to have him plead guilty, keep his mouth shut, and throw himself on the mercy of the court." Ensign Dibble cheerfully agreed, even though he knew that in a completely unexplained case of assault on a superior officer, the mercy of the court would certainly be severely tempered by justice.

When the air group returned from the morning flight, Tony took his usual station just forward of the island, a wheel chock in each hand, waiting for his plane to land. Tony helped Commander Cue with every landing, hitching his shoulders one way or the other in reply to the Landing Signal Officer's paddle waving, and coming up on his tip toes at just the right instant for the wheels to touch gently down on deck.

Between the Commander and Tony, they did an expert job of it. They got a "Roger" from "Paddles" all the way up the groove, and their hook snagged #2 wire with the wheels straddling the white line down the center of the deck.

As Commander Cue taxied briskly up to his parking spot forward of the barriers, Tony rammed the chocks under the wheels, drew his hand across his throat in the cut signal, and scrambled up on the wing alongside the cockpit to watch the Commander fill in the squawk sheet.

Commander Cue was reaching out to shake Tony's hand before he cast loose his safety belt. "You saved my life, kid," he said, and added that a commendation at meritorious mast would be forthcoming. Tony muttered something about probably having to be up before the mast anyway for something else besides a commendation.

Right after "secure" from flight quarters, Tony headed for the incinerator, where he found Fatso and his cronies in a hilarious mood. Tony was hailed as "Man of the Year" when he stuck his head in the door. The incident at the catapult had nothing to do with the award.

"I laughed so hard I could hardly run," said Fatso, "after you clouted him in the ass with that broom."

"He looked like he was going to blow his main high-pressure gasket," said Satchelaft.

"It ain't funny for me now," said Tony soberly. "He put me on the report!"

All faces clouded up at this news and there were ominous mutterings from all hands. Certain statements were made which might not have been cleared for publication if submitted to the Pentagon. Epithets were hurled which had derogatory implications toward Lieutenant Commander T. Tuttle-Taylor's ancestors, and indicating that he probably sat in church scratching himself while his parents were getting married.

"You'd better get yourself a good counsel son," said Satchelaft. "I'll betcha Commander Cue would defend you."

"He ain't eligible," said Scuttlebutt, who had been the accused in several courts-martial and was therefore an expert on legal matters. "That new law says you gotta have a qualified lawyer, so you'll probably be stuck with this Ensign Dibble. He ain't too bad though—last week he beat the rap for that guy in the galley who clobbered Commissar Jones."

Wheels were spinning inside Fatso's head and now his face began to light up and he said, "Too bad I ain't a lawyer. We could cook that legal beagle's goose so he'd never bother anybody on this ship again . . . maybe we can do it anyway."

"How we gonna do it, Fatso?" asked several eager voices.

"The Exec hates the hell out of Tuttle-Taylor," said Fatso. "He's always butting into the Commander's business and quoting new laws about how to run the ship."

"You can put that in the Plan of the Day," said Scuttlebutt.

"Look, Tony," said Fatso, "I was up on deck this morning and saw that whole thing happen. I think if I explain it right to the Commander, you'll come out of this smelling of roses. You just leave the whole thing to me."

That afternoon Fatso had an audience with his old shipmate, the Commander. The Exec sent for Commander Cue to join the meeting and the three of them were closeted together for some time. When the conference broke up they all had smug looks on their faces like sailors on liberty who have just outfoxed the Senior Shore Patrol Officer.

Next morning when the report cases lined up on the flight deck in front of the rostrum where the Captain was about to hold mast as chief magistrate of the ship, Tony was the first man in line.

"Willfully and maliciously striking his superior officer," read the master-at-arms.

For a brief instant the Captain's judicial manner gave way to a look of surprise and shock. "What were the circumstances?" he asked gravely.

Lieutenant Commander T. Tuttle-Taylor stepped forward and said, "Captain, the assault was perpetrated against me with no provocation. It was done right up here on the flight deck in broad daylight, in front of dozens of witnesses. It was a flagrant case that could undermine discipline on the whole ship."

"This is a very serious business," said the Captain. "What led up to the assault?"

"Nothing led up to it sir. It was entirely unprovoked and without warning."

"Did you see him coming at you?" asked the Captain.

"No sir. The attack was delivered from behind my back."

"Did he use his fists on you?"

"No sir. He struck me with a blunt instrument."

"Any other details?" asked the Captain.

"That's all there was to it sir. I was going peaceably about the ship that morning minding my own business and this completely unprovoked assault was delivered from the rear."

68

The Captain turned to Tony and said, "This is a serious charge against you, young man. Under the new code I am required to warn you that anything you say may be used against you and you have a legal right to refuse to answer any questions. Do you wish to explain your conduct?"

Before Tony could say anything, Ensign Dibble stepped forward and said, "Captain, I am a qualified lawyer and I have been detailed to defend this man. As his counsel I have advised him to stand on his legal right and to make no statement."

"No statement?" said the Captain incredulously. The Old Man had grown up in the Navy, where 99 per cent of the disciplinary cases were thrashed out in open hearing before the mast and were usually settled there to the satisfaction of both the United States and the errant sailor. He was not yet used to the new code under which a sailor who fails to turn out at reveille is entitled to a lawyer and an appeal to the Supreme Court if the master-at-arms speaks roughly to him about it.

Tony glanced miserably at his legal adviser, scanned the grave faces surrounding him, and for lack of any better advice decided to string along with the counsel appointed to defend him.

The Captain said, "Well, young man, under the circumstances, there is nothing I can do but give you a general court-martial— next case." Tony retired to the end of the line, his faith in Fatso considerably shaken.

When all the disciplinary cases had been disposed of, the Executive Officer said, "We have one case for meritorious mast this morning, Captain."

"That's fine," said the Captain. "I prefer that kind of cases." Then, as Tony stepped forward, he said, "What? You again?"

While the Executive Officer recounted Tony's action on the catapult the day before, the wheels were going around inside the Captain's head and he thought he began to detect the odor of a small skunk in this deal.

Now, Hear This!

When the Executive Officer had finished, the Captain said, "I saw that incident myself. It was a very brave deed and it saved the life of the pilot as well as one jet airplane. I'm going to recommend you for a medal, son."

Things were happening too fast for Tony, who didn't know very much about military justice anyway. He had never heard of the case in which Napoleon awarded one of his generals a Croix de Guerre for winning a battle and in the next breath ordered him to be shot because he had disobeyed orders to win it. All Tony could do was to stammer his thanks, and wonder if the medal would get him any time off for good behavior at the court-martial.

Then Commander Cue stepped forward and said, "Captain, I am this man's squadron commander, and I would like to ask Commander T. Tuttle-Taylor a few questions before we close this hearing."

"Go ahead," said the Captain.

"Commander," said Cue, "are you willing to swear that the necessary criminal intent was present when Kane made this alleged assault upon you?"

"I object," said Tuttle-Taylor, in his courtroom manner. "That question calls for an opinion, and besides, a properly qualified attorney has been appointed to represent the culprit. You have no right to interfere with counsel's handling of his case."

"Mr. Tuttle-Taylor," said the Captain, "I don't know what the lawyers would say about this but one thing I do know for sure. In the Navy I've served in for the past thirty years, a squadron commander had a responsibility to look out for the rights of his men, and on my ship I expect him to fulfill that responsibility. Go ahead with your questions, Commander Cue."

"Will you please tell the Captain just where you were struck," asked Cue.

"I have already testified I was struck behind my back."

"Yes, I know that—but where? Was it a vital spot?"

"The impact covered a large area," said Tuttle-Taylor.

"Was the blow struck above or below your shoulders?"

"Below," said Tuttle-Taylor.

I have reason to believe the witness is mistaken," said the squadron commander, "and that blow landed *above* the shoulders."

"I guess *I* know where I got hit," said Tuttle-Taylor. "If that blow had been in the head, it would have killed me."

"I still say the blow landed *above* the shoulders due to the unmilitary posture in which the Lieutenant Commander was standing," insisted Cue. "I think the best way to clear up this important point, Captain, is to have him demonstrate the position he was in when the blow was struck."

The Captain approved this suggestion and as Lieutenant Commander T. Tuttle-Taylor stooped over and demonstrated, Commander Cue observed, "I ask you to note, Captain, that the aspect of Lieutenant Commander Tuttle-Taylor which is now presented to view bears no insignia of rank."

The Captain took judicial notice of this point.

"Commander Tuttle-Taylor," said Cue, as the Legal Officer straightened up, "do you know what a sea bat is?"

"Of course I do," said Tuttle-Taylor.

"Have you ever seen one?"

"No, but this man here had one in a box . . ."

It was all clear to the Captain now. He had learned about sea bats the hard way himself as an Ensign on the old *Langley* twenty years ago. "There is no need for further questioning in this case," said the Captain. Then clearing his throat he said, "From the evidence brought out this morning it is clear that this man Kane has conducted himself toward one of his superior officers in a manner which cannot be overlooked."

"I agree with you absolutely, Captain," said Tuttle-Taylor. "Simple justice, as well as military law requires that appropriate action be taken."

Now, Hear This!

"Right," said the Captain. "Mr. Tuttle-Taylor, I want you to draw up a legal paper in this case that will have no loopholes in it. I want a detailed description of what Kane did, with time, place, date, and all pertinent circumstances—something that will stand up under close scrutiny."

"Yessir, yessir. I'll frame a specification that he can't squirm out of under the charge of assaulting his superior officer."

The Captain cocked a weather-beaten eye at the legal officer and said, "You seem to misunderstand me, Mr. Tuttle-Taylor. I consider that incident for which you have reported Kane, although perhaps technically an offense against military law, to be merely a case of rendering an improper salute to his superior officer. There will be no court-martial in connection with this offense. What I want you to write up is not a charge, but a recommendation for a medal. Consult with Commander Cue and get all the necessary details for the citation. Look up the regulations and get the proper phraseology—and see to it that you have all the papers up in my cabin and ready for signature before noon."

"Bu—but—Aye aye, Sir," stammered the legal officer.

"Mast cases dismissed," said the Executive Officer, leaving T. Tuttle-Taylor with his mouth ajar and all four of his cheeks pink.

Down in the incinerator after mast, Satchelaft handed Fatso ten dollars and said, "Well, I guess you're right, Fatso, these double-dome sailors we're getting nowadays aren't too different from what we used to be."

⚓ CHAPTER FOUR

The Dumb Parrot

ONE DAY at sea, Sparky Wright, electronic technician first class, tinkered around in the incinerator compartment, repairing a squawk box of the ship's public announcing system, while Fatso looked on with interest. Sparky had the guts of the box spread out on a tarpaulin, trouble shooting for defective parts.

"These squawk boxes are tricky gadgets," observed Sparky, as he discarded a burned-out coil.

"I'll bet it keeps you busy fixing all the squawk boxes on the ship. Must be hundreds of them," said Fatso, who hadn't really been busy since the Japs surrendered.

"I got a lot more than squawk boxes to take care of," replied Sparky. "All the sound equipment in the ship is in my department. I got the loudspeakers in the radio sets and all the telephones too."

"Say," said Fatso, "I was reading in the papers about that wire-tapping deal in New York when the cops busted up that big gang of hoods. Do you know anything about that kind of stuff—wire taps, bugs, and tape recorders?"

"I know all about it," said Sparky modestly. "I used to work for

73

Now, Hear This!

the phone company."

"They say they got microphones and recorders now that you can hide in a match box," observed Fatso.

"Sure," said Sparky, "we got some of that stuff on this here ship in the radar sets—little transistors about the size of a peanut that do the job of a full-sized vacuum tube. Why, that influence fuse in our anti-aircraft projectiles has a transmitting *and* receiving set in a space as big as a gal's compact."

"Gee," said Fatso, "you mean to say you can put a whole radio set in a tiny space like that? Receiver, loudspeaker, and all?"

"No, not quite," said Sparky, as he secured the loudspeaker diaphragm back in place. "Those are miniature *radar* sets I'm talking about and they don't have loudspeakers. There's a limit to how small you can make a loudspeaker. If it's too small it won't stir up enough air to make sound waves. But they're making them smaller all the time. I got one about the size of a silver dollar that works pretty good. Now hand me that cover, Fatso and we'll have this job finished."

As Sparky was packing up his tools he observed, "Now I gotta go fix the telephone in that guy Commissar Jones' cubbyhole."

Fatso's face clouded up into an angry scowl. He erupted a string of unprintable epithets and said, "I wouldn't fix nothing for that son of a bitch."

"Neither would I," agreed Sparky, "except his telephone or squawk box—I gotta do that. What have *you* got against him, Fatso?"

"The same thing that everybody else on the ship has—he put me on the report once for having liquor aboard and besides that, he's just a no goodnik."

"I know how you feel," said Sparky. "I got some things to square with him too. I don't trust him half as far as I can sling the starboard anchor. If I can ever help you fix him, just let me know. He's the worst friend I got on this ship."

The Dumb Parrot

Several days later Fatso, Satchelaft, and Sparky were strolling along the water front in Genoa when they came to a pet shop where a venerable-looking parrot was doping off in the window. "Let's stop in here and take a look," said Fatso. "I've always wanted to own a parrot."

The proprietor greeted them effusively and Fatso asked to see some parrots.

"Ah," said the shop keeper with a shrug, "so sorry—no gotta parrots."

"What about that one in the window?" asked Fatso.

"You no want him," said the proprietor apologetically, "heeza no good."

"AWK," said the parrot indignantly, suspending himself upside down from the top of the cage and eyeing the three sailors coldly.

"That'sa all he ever say—justa 'AWK'," said the proprietor. "But I gotta some nicea canaries."

"No," said Fatso, "I want a parrot. That one in the window *looks* pretty good. Maybe I can teach him to talk."

"I try for three years," said the shopkeeper, "but all he ever say is AWK. He'sa justa no good."

Satchelaft brushed his finger across the bars of the cage trying to arouse the bird's curiosity. "Look out!" yelled the shopkeeper as the bird made a vicious slash with his beak. Satchelaft let out a howl of pain, followed by a blast of seafaring language and held up a finger covered with blood.

The parrot hung by one claw from the far side of the cage, glared balefully at Satchelaft and said "AWK" in a very insulting way.

"I guess you're right, Tony," said Fatso. "He wouldn't make a good pet. Come on, Sparky, let's get out of here before that chicken tears Satchelaft's arm off and hits him over the head with it."

But as the three were leaving the shop Fatso suddenly stopped dead in his tracks with the expression on his face that always accompanied the birth of an idea. "Sa-a-a-y—wait a minute," he said. "This bird might have possibilities that we could make something out of."

"Sure. Let's take him back to the ship and make hash out of him," suggested Satchelaft.

"AWK," sneered the parrot.

"Maybe I got a better idea than that," said Fatso. "What'll you sell that bird for, Tony?"

"I geeve heem to you for nothing," said Tony. "Heeza no good. But the cage costa fifteen dollars."

"It's a deal," said Fatso, hauling out his wallet and handing over the money.

As Fatso lugged the cage down to the dock, Satchelaft and Sparky hinted broadly that he must have gone nuts. In the *Okinawa's* boat on the way back to the ship, "Pete," as Fatso had christened the parrot, severely nipped the fingers of several sailors and snarled "AWK" belligerently at everyone who paid any attention to him.

"What good is a bloodthirsty bird like that?" demanded Sparky.

"Just wait till we get back aboard," replied Fatso, "and I'll tell you. I got plans for Pete."

Back on the ship, Fatso hung Pete's cage in a corner of the incinerator compartment and said, "Sparky, between you, me and Satchelaft, we can do something with that bird."

"How about my idea of making hash?" demanded Satchelaft.

"AWK," declared Pete cocking a scornful eye at Satchelaft.

"Look," said Fatso, "if we could teach this guy to talk, I'll bet we could get a lot of dough for him."

"Sure," replied Sparky, "but that Eyetalian shopkeeper said he'd been trying for three years and never got nowhere. What makes you think you can?"

"He hasn't got the technical know-how that you and I have,"

76

said Fatso. "I think if we go about it right, we can have this bird talking like a phonograph in a couple of days."

"I don't know nothing about teaching birds to talk," said Sparky. "And neither do you."

"No—but you know a lot about *loudspeakers*, don't ya?"

"Sure—what has that got to do with it?"

"How about wiring this dumb chicken up for sound?" asked Fatso.

"Hunh?" said Sparky, "whaddaya mean?"

"I mean, fit that cage up with some of those things you were telling me about the other day, so it will sound like Pete is talking."

"Well," said Sparky dubiously, "I suppose I could put a small pick-up mike in there—something about the size of a pencil that would fit inside that perch he sits on. You could hook that into the ship's public announcing system so whenever he says 'AWK' everybody on the ship would hear it. What good would that be?"

"None," said Fatso. "We want it to work the other way around. Why can't we put a miniature loudspeaker in the cage? You can hide the wires so nobody will see it, and hook it up so a guy in another compartment can talk into a mike and it will sound like Pete is doing the talking."

Sparky's eyes began to light up with interest at this challenging technical problem. "Maybe you *have* got something there, Fatso," he said. "I've got a speaker the size of a watch that we could hide inside that brass gimmick at the top of the cage that the hook fastens into. I can run a wire through the hook and put a hand mike wherever you want it . . . but anybody who took a real close look inside that cage might spot our loudspeaker."

"Anybody who puts his puss close enough to that cage to take a real good look," declared Satchelaft, "is going to be wondering where the hell the other half of his nose went instead of thinking about loudspeakers."

"AWK," said Pete emphatically, grabbing his perch in his beak

Now, Hear This!

and almost biting it in two.

"So he would," agreed Sparky. "We could even make a two-way intercom out of this. I'll put a mike in there to pick up anything you say to Pete, run it to a wire recorder, and we can play that back through the loudspeaker. That way Pete would repeat whatever you say to him, just like a parrot is supposed to."

"Now we're getting somewhere," said Fatso.

Sparky began to wax enthusiastic. "I can rig this up easy. These miniature speakers sound kind of tinny, and they ain't too good on the low frequencies, but that's the way a parrot sounds anyway."

"AWK," commented Pete tinnily.

"Yeah," said Fatso. "We got one big hitch though. He just sits on that perch doping off most of the time. That wouldn't look right when he is supposed to be talking. He ought to be climbing around kinda lively."

"I can fix that too," said Sparky, who was now interested in more than just the scientific aspects of the project. "I'll just run a wire from the speaker to the perch and ground it. Whenever the speaker comes on, he'll get a little shot of juice to wake him up."

"Make it a helluva stiff shot," advised Satchelaft surveying his damaged finger.

"AWK," objected Pete, glaring balefully at Satchelaft.

"No, we gotta be reasonable," said Sparky. "We don't want to knock him flat on his ass. We just want to tickle him a bit, and get him stirring around the way a gabby parrot usually does."

Next day Sparky brought his tool box up to the incinerator and Pete was dumped out of his cage unceremoniously into a large tin ammunition canister. He spent the next couple of hours thrashing around trying to claw his way out, hammering at the tin with his beak and snarling obscene "AWKs" in an infuriated manner while Fatso and Sparky installed his intercom system. If Pete had been able to really talk during this period, his remarks certainly could not have been sent through the U.S. Mails. When Fatso dumped

78

The Dumb Parrot

him back in the cage again, Pete, exhausted by his efforts, climbed up on the perch, let out a few injured "AWKs" and went back to sleep again.

"So far, so good. You can't see either the mike or the speaker," observed Sparky, as he unscrewed the original hook on the cage and replaced it with one fashioned from a small brass conduit out of a radar set, having conductors hidden inside it. By hanging this hook on any metal frame of the ship you completed the circuit Sparky had rigged up to a black box containing a recorder, amplifier, and play-back circuit.

"Whaddaya say, Sparky?" asked Fatso, as he hung the cage on a beam. "Ready for a trial run?"

"Okay, here goes," said Sparky. Getting as close to the cage as he could and still be out of reach of Pete's claws, he said, "Polly wanta cracker?" and flipped the switch energizing the playback circuit.

From the loudspeaker at the top of the cage, but seemingly from Pete himself came back the words, "Polly wanta cracker?"

Pete bounced straight up in the air with both eyes bugging out, emitted an outraged "AWK," and began scrambling around the cage clawing at the bars with his beak quivering.

"We gotta cut down a bit on the voltage to the agitator circuit," announced Sparky judicially. "We almost fried him that time, feathers and all."

"AWK," agreed Pete emphatically in an injured tone.

By trial and error, Sparky soon got the voltage adjusted properly without quite knocking Pete cold in the process. The speaker circuit worked perfectly, repeating everything back word for word at the flip of a switch.

"We better let Pete take a blow for a while now," observed Fatso. "Come back tonight, Sparky and we'll give this thing an official full power run when the boys drop in after taps for steaks."

"Okay," said Sparky. "I'll get here early and we'll put that black

Now, Hear This!

box behind the incinerator where nobody will see it. And I've got another circuit I want to add to our hookup. With what we got now all he can do is repeat stuff back. I'll hook up a hand mike to the black box and we can make him give out with some original ideas or even answer questions."

"Okay Pal. See you tonight," said Fatso.

Scuttlebutt was the first one of Fatso's cronies to arrive that night. "Hiya Fatso," he said. "Didja teach that dumb bird anything today?"

"Just try him and see," said Fatso.

"Polly wanna cracker?" queried Scuttlebutt.

The carefully adjusted agitator circuit woke Pete up with a mild start and he "repeated," "Polly wanna cracker?"

"Gee, that *is* good," said Scuttlebutt.

"Gee, that *is* good," echoed Pete, taking a swipe with his beak at his charged perch.

"By golly, he even imitates your voice," said Scuttlebutt.

"It just takes a little patience and know-how," observed Fatso, and Pete added weight to this observation by repeating it.

Scuttlebutt was amazed and enthusiastic at this exhibition.

It was the same story as each of Fatso's other pals arrived. Pete was a sensation, repeating back long phrases word for word and mimicking voices perfectly. By expert work on the play back switch, Sparky confined Pete's "remarks" to repeating those queries and statements addressed directly to him. He also jolted Pete off his perch several times and kept him moving around the cage rather briskly. After half an hour of this, Sparky flipped the speaker switch off, and Pete, after feeling the perch gingerly, climbed back on it and lapsed into a moody silence.

"I guess he's tired now," said Fatso, as several queries aimed at Pete remained unanswered. For the next few minutes there were enthusiastic comments on Pete's performance and finally Scuttlebutt said, "By golly Fatso, I never thought you could teach that

The Dumb Parrot

dumb bird to talk."

This was the opening which Sparky, behind the incinerator, had been waiting for. He squeezed his hand mike button popping Pete down off the perch and demanded, "Who you calling dumb, sailor?"

The men's jaws dropped open and all heads snapped around to look at Pete. After a moment of incredulous silence Scuttlebutt demanded, "Whu . . . whu . . . what was that?"

"You heard me, *stupid*," snarled Pete.

All hands goggled—their eyes bugging out. Then a knowing grin spread over Scuttlebutt's face and he said, "Oh—I get it. But I never knew you was a ventriloquist, Fatso."

"I ain't," said Fatso, at the same time that another commotion broke loose in the cage and Pete sneered. "Look at the rubber swab handle that's calling *me* a Charley McCarthy."

There could be no doubt whatever that this remark came direct from the cage.

Every one of Fatso's cronies made the same comment all in one breath, "Well I'll be Gah-damned."

"Oh—you think that's pretty good?" inquired Pete, suspending himself athwartships on the far side of the cage. "Then lissen to this," he said, and burst into the old sea chantey. "What You Going To Do With A Drunken Sailor?"

"He's terrific," breathed Beer Bottle, in an awed voice.

"You ain't heard nothing yet, Bub," averred Pete, climbing around the cage in an orbit parallel to the deck and eyeing his charged perch suspiciously—"Ask me some questions."

"Go on," said Fatso, "ask him something. Make it tough. Give him a problem in arithmetic."

"How much is three times seven?" demanded Scuttlebutt.

"Twenty-one," said Pete. "Count it up on your fingers if you can't do it any other way."

To say that Fatso's pals were dumbfounded would be a gross

understatement. They were the most flabbergasted bunch of sailors who had put to sea since Noah cast off the moorings of the Ark.

"Why he's colossal," breathed Scuttlebutt. "He's even better than that horse in Virginia I was reading about that's got all them college professors and doctors stumped—the one that shakes his head 'yes' and 'no' and stamps with his foot to count—but this little pigeon even talks back to you and gets sassy about it."

"You could make millions offa him if you put him on television," said Beer Bottle. "I seen a program in the States starring a bird that didn't have half the brains this one has."

"Hunh! There's plenty of them," snorted Pete. "Jack Benny, Milton Berle, Bing Crosby—"

"Why, he's smarter than most of the guys on this ship," declared Scuttlebutt.

At this remark, loud guffaws burst from behind the incinerator and Sparky, unable to contain himself any longer, emerged from his hiding place with a portable mike in his hand. He and Fatso swore the others to secrecy and then explained the whole set-up to the still bewildered sailors.

Scuttlebutt was now so thoroughly convinced of Pete's authenticity that he had to take a look at the loudspeaker—and got an ugly gash in the end of his nose doing it, just as Satchelaft had predicted somebody would.

"Well, we can have a lot of fun with him anyway," said Beer Bottle. "After the word gets around, everybody on the ship will be standing in line to see him—we can charge admission . . ."

"No," said Fatso, "we don't want to commercialize him. Sparky and I have got another idea. We're going to use him to square accounts with Commissar Jones."

"How you gonna do that?" asked Satchelaft eagerly.

"Sell him to Commissar for a lot of dough," said Fatso. "We couldn't get away with this loudspeaker deal forever anyway. But if we work it right and get all hands talking about Pete, I'll bet we can get Commissar to buy him for a couple of hundred bucks."

This idea was greeted with unanimous gleeful approval. Commissar had other "Bad Friends" besides Sparky. Everybody on the ship hated him.

"It will be an easy deal to swing," said Fatso, "*if* we're careful about it."

They spent the next hour laying out detailed plans about how to be careful. Fatso's gang had plenty of experience planning shady enterprises, and one such as this was right down their alley. The Naval War College would have been proud of the thorough and systematic way that they laid this one out, following the classic War College method of estimating the situation, weighing all possible courses of action, and arriving at a decision that took advantage of all pertinent factors, including even Commissar's well-known characteristics as a gyp artist always trying to get something for nothing. When the plan was completed, Fatso said, "He'll go for it hook, line and sinker. He'll draw all his pay off the books and borrow money besides—if anybody on the ship is sucker enough to lend it to him."

Next day Fatso hung Pete's cage outside the incinerator at chow time when the hangar deck was crowded with sailors waiting for "pipe down." This was to be simply a "repeat back" performance on Pete's part with no ad libs or wisecracks put into his mouth by Sparky.

Of course any pet will draw a crowd on the hangar deck, and a talking parrot will draw one anywhere. Pete was soon surrounded by a throng of delighted admirers hailing his mimicry.

Commissar Jones, as master-at-arms of the hangar deck, could be depended upon to poke his nose into any crowd that collected there, and soon that sinister official came bustling up. He barged into the center of the crowd intending simply to find out what they were doing and make them knock it off. Pete's artistry and

83

versatility captured even Commissar's interest for a while. But pretty soon his greedy nature asserted itself. He began counting the house and mentally figuring how much it would bring at two bits a head.

When "pipe down" went and the crowd melted away Commissar said to Fatso, "How much do you want for that bird?"

Fatso considered the question briefly and replied, "Oh—I dunno —I hadn't figured on selling him."

"I'll give you twenty bucks," said Commissar.

Fatso let out a contemptuous snort.

Commissar reviewed his mental arithmetic. At twenty-five cents a head there had been well over twenty dollars just in that one crowd before lunch . . . "I might even make it fifty dollars," he announced.

"He ain't for sale, Bub," said Fatso. "Not at *that* price anyway."

Commissar carried his calculations a little further. During a long week at sea practically every one of the *Okinawa's* 3,000 sailors would pay to see a talented performer like Pete. Six hundred dollars was a conservative estimate of his earning potential. "How about seventy-five dollars, cash on the line?" he asked.

"Hell, you ain't offered me anything like what I paid for him, yet," said Fatso, "and any parrot that talks real good is worth at least two hundred in the States."

Commissar dropped the subject and strolled off. Fatso took Pete back inside the incinerator compartment where Sparky, standing by his black box, asked eagerly, "How did it go?"

"We got him hooked," said Fatso gleefully, "I figure he'll go at least 250—just using the playback routine. If he falls for the other part, he'll put his grandmother in hock for whatever price we want—you go see him today and give him the business."

That afternoon Sparky dropped in to Commissar's cubbyhole "to check up on that squawk box I fixed last week."

"It's working pretty good," said Commissar.

Sparky hooked a volt meter across the squawk box terminals, noted the voltage and said, "By the way Commissar, have you seen that parrot everybody is talking about that Gioninni bought in Genoa for 150 bucks?"

"Yeah," said Commissar. "It ain't a bad bird—but Gioninni got gypped if he paid that much for it. When I was in Panama I could a bought parrots that talk better than that for a hundred bucks."

"Sure—in Panama," said Sparky, "but in the States you can't touch a real good talking parrot for less than two hundred."

"He's pretty good," admitted Commissar. "Maybe you could get two hundred for him."

Sparky assumed a mysterious look, poked his head out of the cubbyhole and peered both ways along the hangar deck. Then closing the door carefully and lowering his voice he said, "That bird is worth a lot more than Gioninni thinks."

"Yeah?" said Commissar. "How come?"

"He can do things Gioninni don't even know about yet," said Sparky. "I looked at that parrot in Genoa the day before Gioninni bought him. The only reason the guy sold him that cheap was because he stole him from a carnival, and had to get rid of him."

Any story of intrigue such as this was grist for Commissar's mill. His interest perked up immediately. "What else can he do besides talk?" he asked eagerly.

Sparky clammed up a bit and assumed a wise look. "You understand of course I ain't telling you this for *nothing*," he said.

"What's your proposition?" asked Commissar.

"After you buy him you gotta split 50-50 with me on whatever dough you make offa him—and I mean radio and TV rights too."

"Sure, that's OK pal," said Commissar. "Now what's the dope?"

"That bird can do a lot more than just talk," said Sparky. "He's got a brain like a human be-an and understands what you say— he can answer questions and work out arithmetic problems in his head. He's a—he's a genius."

"I don't believe it," said Commissar.

"I don't blame you," said Sparky. "But I *know* it's so because I ast him all kinds of stuff in Genoa the day before Gioninni bought him and he gave me the right answers. He even told me how many lira you get for nine dollars and a half."

"You're nuts," declared Commissar, "or else you were drunk that day in Genoa. Why a bird like that would be worth over a thousand bucks."

"He sure would," said Sparky. "But everybody in Genoa knows this bird. That's why the guy who stole him had to sell him to a sailor cheap. If you don't believe what I'm telling you why don't you go up to the incinerator when Gioninni ain't there and see for yourself. Don't let Gioninni catch you doing it though, because if he knew how smart this bird is he'd boost the price."

"That sounds fair enough," said Commissar.

"I'll put seventy-five bucks into this deal to show you how much I believe in it," said Sparky, "you'll have to put up the rest of the cash to buy him. For my seventy-five bucks, and for putting the finger on the deal, you got to agree to give me 50 per cent of the profit. Okay?"

"Sure. I already agreed to that," said Commissar. "But of course I mean *net* profit after all expenses are paid," he added warily. "How can we get Gioninni away from his hangout for an hour or so?"

"I'll take care of that," said Sparky. "I'm fixing a radio set for him. I'll get him down in my shop at ten tomorrow morning and keep him there till eleven. You won't have to worry about anyone else coming to the incinerator because they'll all be at flight quarters then. You just leave it to me—I'll phone you from my shop when the coast is clear."

"Okay," said Commissar. "I'll be waiting."

"There's just one more thing," said Sparky. "The big secret that

Gioninni don't know yet is that you got to call this bird by his right name to get any real answers out of him. When you call him Pete, like Gioninni does, he just repeats the same as any other parrot. But call him *Antonio,* and then he really goes into his act."

"I got it," said Commissar. "I'll expect a call about ten tomorrow."

Next morning Fatso and Sparky checked all Pete's equipment carefully and found it in good order. Sparky boosted the voltage on the agitator circuit a touch and said, "Go on down to my shop now, Fatso, and stay there till I call you." Allowing Fatso time enough to get below he dialed Commissar's cubbyhole and said in a muffled voice, "Okay, Fatso's in my shop now. The coast is clear." Then he squeezed in behind the incinerator with his black box and hand mike to await developments.

Pretty soon the door opened cautiously. Commissar stuck his head in, peered quickly around, stepped inside and closed the door. Pete was doping off as usual on his perch.

"Hello polly," said Commissar.

Pete got a jolt of juice and sprang to life immediatety—"Hello polly," came the reply.

"Polly wanna cracker?" inquired Commissar.

"Polly wanna cracker?" repeated Pete backing off from the perch.

Then Commissar took another look around, approached a little closer to the cage, lowered his voice and said rather dubiously, "Hello *Antonio*—how ya feeling today?"

Sparky cut out the repeater circuit and went into action with the hand mike.

"Hello yourself," growled Pete. "I'm okay, how are you?"

Commissar's jaw dropped and he stood rooted to the deck for an instant. Finally he said, "Well I'll be Gah-dam."

"You sure will be, if the fat wop that runs this place catches you in here talking to me like this," said Pete going into his routine of climbing around the side of the cage and keeping clear of the perch.

Commissar's none too mighty brain reeled at the impact of what he had just found out. He had a fortune within his grasp! He was torn between conflicting emotions of curiosity and greed. He was also a bit overawed in the presence of such a remarkable intellect as Pete's.

Pulling himself together he inquired, "How much is five times three, polly?"

"How much is five times three, polly," mimicked Pete.

"Oh, excuse me *Sir*," said Commissar. "How much is five times three, *Antonio?*"

"Fifteen, you dumb cluck. Anybody knows that," came the answer.

This was enough for Commissar. Impossible though it seemed, the bird performed exactly as Sparky had claimed. Commissar tiptoed softly toward the door, reached for the dog, and then feeling a bit embarrassed at sneaking out unceremoniously like this with a personage such as Pete (or Antonio) giving him the fish eye, he turned and said, "Ah . . . ah . . . er . . . I'll see you later, *Antonio.*"

"Okay. G'bye Pal," said Pete, Antonio, or Sparky, depending on how you look at it, as Commissar disappeared.

Soon Fatso came hurrying back to the incinerator. "We got him hooked all right," chuckled Sparky. "I even had him saying 'sir' to the bird. I'll betcha he'd still believe Pete can talk even if we showed him the whole hook-up now—I'll go see him this afternoon and give him the seventy-five bucks for my part of the deal."

"Don't get too cocky about it," warned Fatso. "This deal is too good to louse up now."

Again at noon that day Fatso hung the cage out on the hangar deck. Word of the parrot's talents had spread all over the ship, so Pete played to a much bigger audience than the day before, sticking entirely to his repeat-back routine. On the outskirts of the crowd with a smug, calculating look on his face was Commissar Jones.

While the performance was going on the Captain came back aboard after a trip to the beach and walking forward from the gangway on the hangar deck, noticed the crowd around the incinerator. As he paused to see what was going on the Marine orderly yelled "Gangway" and the crowd opened up respectfully and let the skipper go right up in front.

Pete was "repeating" a remark which had just been made to him when the Captain got there.

"Good morning, Gioninni," said the Captain affably, "that bird is a good talker."

"Yessir Cap'n," said Fatso.

"Good morning Gioninni, that bird is a good talker," mimicked Pete.

"Remarkable," said the Captain. "Really remarkable."

"Remarkable, really remarkable," echoed Pete.

"I've always wanted a good talking parrot," said the Captain. "How much will you take for him, Gioninni?"

Recognizing the Captain's voice, Sparky, inside the incinerator compartment, cut off the repeat-back switch.

"He ain't for sale, Cap'n," said Fatso hastily.

"I'm willing to pay well for a bird like that," said the Captain.

"Well, Cap'n," said Fatso, "I—just can't sell you this one, sir."

The Captain continued his admiring inspection of Pete and said, "My lady has always wanted a good parrot, too. We will give it a good home if that's what you're worried about."

"Nossir. I ain't worried about *that*, sir," said Fatso.

"I'll give you twice what you paid for it," said the Captain.

Fatso was in a tough spot. When the Captain makes it quite

plain to any ordinary sailor that he wants something very much the sailor usually is happy to oblige the skipper. But of course Fatso was no ordinary sailor and in this case he could see breakers ahead. He didn't want to be impolite to the Captain, but he also didn't want to palm off a gold brick on him and maybe undermine what had been a long and beautiful friendship. He wanted to palm it off on Commissar Jones.

"I'll give you $200 for him," said the Captain as Fatso racked his brains for a way out.

"Captain . . . um . . . er . . ." stammered Fatso, "I . . ."

Here Sparky took charge and got Fatso off the hook. He turned up the agitator control, pressed the button popping Pete straight up in the air and growled, "Son of a BITCH!"

"Harrumph," observed the Captain, "that's not so good."

Then Sparky cut loose with a string of all the four-letter words he could think of, which of course was all such words in the language. It was a blast of purple obscenity that would have gotten you thrown out of any well-run waterfront whorehouse in the Free World.

"My, *My!*" said the Captain. "Such language!"

"Yes *Sir*, Cap'n," said Fatso. "It's awful. That bird wouldn't do for you at all, Cap'n."

"Where did he learn that kind of talk?" demanded the Captain.

"Not from *me*, Sir," said Fatso piously.

"If I heard any sailor on this ship using that kind of language," said the Captain, "I'd put him in the brig for three days on bread and water."

Sparky promptly snapped off the switch and put down his microphone.

"Yes *Sir*, Cap'n," agreed Fatso.

"I'm afraid that isn't the kind of a bird I wanted after all," said the Captain.

"No *Sir*, Cap'n," said Fatso.

The Dumb Parrot

"My lady is pretty broad-minded," observed the Captain. "But she is a religious woman, too. I'm afraid she wouldn't allow that kind of talk in her living room."

"I don't blame her a bit," agreed Fatso as the Captain shoved off.

Commissar Jones had been standing close by while this was going on drinking it all in. He was somewhat shook when he heard Fatso turn down a cool 200 bucks for the bird.

That afternoon Sparky came around to Commissar's cubbyhole and asked, "Howdya make out this morning? Wasn't it just like I told you?"

"No-o-o-o—not quite as good as you said," declared Commissar coolly, "but—pretty good at that."

Sparky hauled seventy-five dollars out of his pocket and asked, "Is it a deal pal? I give you this seventy-five, you put up the rest, and then we own him fifty-fifty after you buy him?"

"I been thinking about this thing," said Commissar. "And I wouldn't be getting a fair shake on that deal. I may have to draw all the money I've got on the books and go up as high as six hundred bucks to buy that bird—I'll cut you in for ten per cent, but that's all."

Sparky, knowing that the net profit on this deal was going to be zero, had a hard time pretending to be reluctant about paring his share of it down from 50 to 10 per cent. But the greedy Commissar didn't notice this, and they finally settled on 10 per cent.

That night, while all of Fatso's cronies were gathered in the incinerator having their regular evening snack, Commissar came in. "Fatso," he said without beating around the bush, "I want to buy that parrot—I'll give you two hundred bucks for him."

Fatso weighed the offer judicially and replied, "Naw—I don't want to sell him."

Commissar produced a roll of bills as big around as a hawser, began counting them and said, "Well how about *three* hundred

—cash on the line?"

An excited buzz among Fatso's friends greeted this offer.

"No-o-o-o," said Fatso. "I just don't want to sell him—and he ain't worth that much anyway."

"I *know* he ain't," declared Commissar emphatically, "but I'm offering it to you anyway, and with no strings attached," he added glancing around the circle of Fatso's cronies to see that all present understood.

"Gee," said Fatso, "I'd kinda hate to part with the little guy. I've gotten to like him. And you can buy lots better parrots than him for that kind of dough."

"Sure I know that," said Commissar realizing that Fatso was weakening, "but I kinda like the little guy too. Tell ya what I'll do, Fatso—I'll give you *four hundred dollars* for him, and that's as high as I'll go."

"Well . . ." said Fatso. "If you want him *that* bad, all right . . . But I'm telling you he isn't worth it and I've seen lots of parrots that can talk better than him. All you guys heard what I'm telling him," he added making a gesture toward his pals, "so there can't be any argument about this deal later."

"Don't worry, Fatso, there won't be no argument," said Commissar peeling off twenty-dollar bills from his roll. "Here y'are Pal, four hundred bucks. He ain't worth it but it's a deal." So saying he handed over the four hundred, lifted the cage off its support and departed with Pete who woke up just long enough to utter a curious "AWK?"

As soon as Commissar was out of earshot pandemonium broke loose in the incinerator. "Fatso, you missed your calling," declared Judge Jenks. "You oughta be selling gold bricks to the sharpshooters along Broadway."

"Did you get your equipment out of the cage, Sparky?" asked Fatso.

"I sure did," said Sparky. "It's all right here in my tool box.

And believe me I'm going to be a hard man for that guy Jones to find the rest of this cruise. I think I'll move my bunk up on the bridge near the Captain's sea cabin—now gimme back my seventy-five bucks, Fatso, and we're all square."

"Here's two hundred," said Fatso. "We split fifty-fifty on this deal."

Commissar was not too concerned about "Antonio's" moody silence that first night. He figured that the strange surroundings in his cubbyhole accounted for the bird's reticence, and that he would loosen up in the morning. After a few futile attempts to strike up a friendly conversation and getting no reply except "AWK," he covered the cage and turned in.

But when Pete sat there eyeing him suspiciously the next morning and refusing to make any comment except "AWK," Commissar began to get impatient. "Come on, *Antonio*," he demanded, "*say* something."

Pete stirred about uneasily on his perch as if suspecting he was about to get a shock, let out a nervous AWK, and lapsed back into a sullen silence.

Commissar spent the whole morning pleading, cajoling, and finally threatening. It was no use. Pete had clammed up like a wooden Indian. The only effect Commissar's badgering and brow-beating had was to cause Pete's usually defiant expression to give way to an apprehensive and harried one. Commissar dialed Sparky's phone a dozen times, but Sparky was always "out on a job."

By mid-afternoon the situation in the cubbyhole had become tense. Commissar sat at his desk glowering evilly at Pete, and the poor bird sat on his perch with a bewildered look saying nothing, but expecting a hell of a jolt of juice any minute.

"Come on you blankety-blank four-flushing son of a bitch," roared Commissar. "Open up and *say* something . . . ANTONIO."

Now, Hear This!

The chief master-at-arms in the next cubbyhole began to wonder who this errant sailor Antonio was, that his assistant had been putting the blast on for the past hour. He concluded Antonio must be a pretty tough character to hold out so long against Commissar. As Commissar's tirade became louder and louder, the flagrantly illegal threats of bodily harm to the uncommunicative Antonio shocked even the chief master-at-arms. He began to fear that his helper was becoming overzealous, exceeding the Uniform Code of Military Justice, and decided to caution him later to be more discreet in enforcing discipline and questioning culprits.

Finally Pete, exhausted by his ordeal, doped off and went to sleep. This was too much for Commissar. He reached over, grabbed the cage, rattled the bars, and then let out a bellow of rage as Pete took a vicious bite out of his thumb. Commissar belted the cage with his other hand, denting the side with the door in it out of shape, knocking Pete back against the far side and receiving another ugly wound in that hand.

Commissar saw red now. With a string of oaths, he grabbed the cage by the hook, burst out of his cubbyhole, and ran aft, hotly pursued by the chief master-at-arms who was convinced by now that his helper had gone nuts.

Back at the stern Commissar shook the cage violently.

"For the last time . . . are you going to talk, ANTONIO—PLEASE," he demanded.

"AWK," protested Pete.

Commissar hauled off and flung the cage, Pete and all, far out over the stern. The heave threw Pete against the damaged door, which flew open and out came Pete, twenty feet in the air and ten feet astern of the ship. With a stiff breeze blowing and the ship making 15 knots, Pete, who was pretty rusty on his flying, had a hard struggle getting back aboard. He finally made it just as the CMAA was leading Commissar down to sick bay for an interview with the senior medico. Perching on a 20-millimeter barrel,

The Dumb Parrot

Pete sat there gasping AWK while a large crowd collected.

Soon Fatso came rushing out wearing heavy leather gloves followed by Satchelaft with a canvas sea bag. Pete, too exhausted to fly any more, put up only token resistance against recapture but pinched one of Fatso's fingers even through the heavy leather before being popped into the sea bag and taken back to the incinerator.

"Whaddaya gonna do with him now?" asked Satchelaft.

"Keep him," said Fatso. "Commissar thrun him away and tried to drownd him. We saved him, so he's ours again now. Jump down to the carpenter shop, Satchelaft, and get Chips to make us another cage."

From inside the bag came a muffled "AWK, *say* something, ANTONIO, AWK."

"By golly we'll teach this pigeon to talk yet," said Fatso, "he's beginning to learn already."

⚓ CHAPTER FIVE

Rubbish on the Riviera

As THE MOON rose over the Mediterranean, the U.S. Sixth Fleet steamed along south of Malta in cruising formation. The senior officer afloat was Admiral "Bread-and-Water" Biggs, his flag flying in the cruiser *Salem*. In company with the flagship were the giant aircraft carriers *Okinawa* and *Iwo Jima* and a circular screen of twenty destroyers. U.S. control of the seas in that area was unchallenged at this moment, and the fleet had squared away on the course for the night, with most of the officers and men asleep in their bunks.

On board the *Okinawa*, down in the incinerator compartment, Fatso and his cronies were gathered around the big trash furnace for their usual evening critique of global strategy.

Beer Bottle, munching on a juicy steak, was thumbing through a slick-paper Parisian magazine, when the center page spread brought him up with a round turn.

"Boy-oh-boy-oh-boy! Look at this!" he said, displaying a picture of a dozen scantily clad bathing beauties sunning themselves on a well-equipped private beach. "That's what I call almost 'bare aft'—An informal beach party at Mrs. Worthington's Villa on the

Riviera, it says here. Hey, ain't that where we're going next—the Riviera?"

"Yeah," replied Fatso. "But all you'll see of Mrs. Worthington's little pad is right here in that magazine. It's out of bounds except for officers. Nothing from this here incinerator compartment will get within hailing distance of that joint."

"There's plenty of other gals around Nice," observed Scuttlebutt. "You been there before haven't you, Fatso?"

"If it's a seaport I've been there, Bub," replied Fatso, who had four hashmarks on his sleeve. "I've got a whole book full of numbers in Nice from last year when I was there on the *Wasp*. You want a blonde, redhead or brunette?"

"We're going to need that book, Fatso," said Judge Jenks, the Executive Officer's yeoman. "We're due in there a couple of days before the Fourth of July. That's one time when the French go all out for the U.S. sailors. They celebrate it like one of their own holidays. They have a big parade up the main drag, and they heave a fancy-dress ball in the Casino that night for the sailors in the fleet. They tell me it's quite a clambake with free eats and champagne."

"I went to it last year," said Fatso. "Most fun I've had with my clothes on since the day Commissar Jones fell down the forward elevator. I went with a gal we called the Antelope—because she could run so fast."

"What good would it do you to go with a gal like that?" demanded Beer Bottle, surveying Fatso's vast bulk.

"She liked me," said Fatso with dignity, "so she didn't run as hard as she could. You guys should all go to that ball, it's apt to be the best party of the cruise. It starts on the 4th of July but nobody sobers up from it till after Bastille Day on the 14th."

"Don't worry," said Beer Bottle. "Everybody knows about that whoop-de-doo. It's like an artist's ball in Paris. The main reason I put in for duty in the Med was to see if what I heard about those ten days in Nice is so."

"There's one angle we'd better be thinking about," observed Judge Jenks, who did all the long range planning for the crowd. "The *Iwo Jima* gets in the same time we do. Somebody's got to get ashore as soon as the hook goes down and line the dames up. If that crowd of swabs from the *Iwo Jima* get ashore first, we will be out of luck."

"Just leave it to me," said Fatso, "I'll get ashore *before* the hook goes down. I got a drag with the helicopter pilot. I'll go over in the whirly bird when they take the mail orderly ashore. I'll call up the Antelope and get dates for the whole bunch."

Having settled that matter and eaten all the steaks, the board of strategy adjourned.

Next morning on the Riviera, Mrs. Susannah Worthington paced the sun room of her palatial villa while her secretary put through a call to the U.S. Embassy in Paris. When the Ambassador was on the line, the secretary handed Mrs. Worthington the phone.

"Hello Georgie dahling," she cooed, "I want you to do a very great favor for me."

"What is it *this* time Susie?" asked the Ambassador, in a way that indicated he wouldn't be surprised by even the most outrageous demands from Mrs. W.

"The American Fleet is coming in to Nice next week and I want to give a little party for them on the first of July. I want you to get me the top Admiral in the Fleet for my party."

The Ambassador knew, of course, that Susie's "little" party would be a gigantic affair with troupes of entertainers from London and Paris. He also knew that every rival hostess on the Riviera would try to make a bum out of Susie by snagging the Admiral, if she could, and throwing a bigger and better party. "Why don't you just send him an invitation, Susie?" asked the Ambassador innocently.

"Don't be stupid, George," said Mrs. Worthington. "Everybody from Villefranche to Cannes wants him for their parties. He'll get dozens of invitations and you know how unpredictable and erratic these Admirals are. He might accept the wrong ones and get mixed up with all sorts of impossible people if you don't steer him right."

"Oh, I don't know about that," said the Ambassador. "After all, an Admiral ought to know how to take care of himself by now. I don't see that it's my business to arrange his social calendar."

"Georgie. Stop being difficult about this. When the fleet visits a place like Nice it's top-level State Department business and you know it. You had to approve before they could even come here. So it's your duty to see that the Admiral meets the right people. You remember the awful mess we had a couple of years ago when that Admiral showed up at the Prefect's grand gala with a notorious madam in tow."

"The only trouble," said the Ambassador reminiscently, "was that so many of her best customers were in the receiving line, and she should have been more discreet about recognizing them. And besides, it wasn't an Admiral, it was only a Lieutenant Commander."

"Well, what's the difference?" demanded Mrs. Worthington. "Sailors, Lieutenant Commanders, or Admirals. They're all the same when they get ashore. Now go ahead and do what I want you to—will you, Georgie?"

"All right, Susie, I will," said the Ambassador, knowing from long experience that Susie hadn't taken no for an answer (or given it either, for that matter) since she left the Ziegfeld chorus twenty years ago to marry the Worthington millions.

Later that day a dispatch went out from the Embassy to the flagship of the fleet "suggesting" that Admiral Biggs keep the evening of the first of July open for Mrs. Worthington's party.

99

Now, Hear This!

This was perfectly OK with Admiral Biggs, because he had heard of Mrs. Worthington's fabulous parties and was hoping she might heave one for him.

Dispatches also went out from the flagship *Salem* that day to all ships in company, giving detailed instructions for the forthcoming visit to the Riviera. These instructions covered liberty hours, shore patrol regulations, and among other things, contained a very strict injunction to throw nothing—repeat, *nothing*—overboard while anchored in Nice.

There had been unpleasant international complications in the past caused by visiting warships littering the beach of this world-famous resort with drifting rubbish, and Admiral Biggs did not propose to have a repetition of it this time. The orders stated that CO's would be held personally responsible, and it was well known that anyone who was held personally responsible by Admiral "Bread-and-Water" Biggs was in a hell of a spot. The Admiral had never heaved a four-stripe captain into the brig on bread and water, but he had other ways of letting them know when he was displeased with them. The same dispatch notified the *Okinawa* that on 2 July, Admiral Biggs would hold his annual inspection of that vessel. This was a sad blow to the crew, because it meant the first couple of days in Nice would be occupied with shining the ship up for the great event and liberty hours for the crew would be curtailed accordingly.

But late that afternoon an even worse blow fell. The *Salem* and *Iwo Jima* broke off from the rest of the fleet and headed for Nice, leaving the others to continue maneuvers for four more days while the *Salem* and *Iwo Jima* went in early.

That night in the incinerator compartment, the morale of Fatso's gang was at a low ebb. "Those fairweather swabs on the *Iwo Jima* get all the gravy," complained Beer Bottle Bates, wiping the steak gravy off his chin. "Why does this Admiral always give that bucket the breaks?"

Rubbish on the Riviera

"When he plays golf with her Skipper," said Scuttlebutt Grogan, "the Skipper lets him win. Our Skipper beats the hell out of him."

"That's certainly going to gum up the 4th of July ball for us," said Beer Bottle. "Those guys from the *Iwo Jima* will line up all the dames that ain't in the old ladies' home before we ever get in there. We'll just be out of luck."

"I been saving up for two pay days on account of this visit to Nice," said Scuttlebutt. "But with the *Iwo Jima* and *Salem* both getting in there ahead of us, I might just as well of wasted my money on savings bonds."

"You guys can quit worrying about that," said Fatso. "Just leave everything to me. As soon as we get in I'll call up the Antelope and everything will be all set. She's head of the barmaids' union and what she says goes around Nice. One word from me and she'll get all her gals to sack those lugs from the *Iwo Jima* and go to the ball with us. It's a lucky break for you guys you've got Uncle Fatso to look out for you."

There was enough truth in this last statement so that all hands present just munched on Fatso's steaks and let it pass unchallenged.

"The only thing I'm worried about," said Fatso, "is, we got this admiral's inspection coming up. That's going to put me on the spot because how can I get this place cleaned up with everybody on the ship dragging tons of stuff up here to be burned? Old Bread-and-Water didn't like this place last time he inspected and he's got a memory like an elephant. If it ain't shined up this time, I'll get restricted sure. I'm gonna close this incinerator down two days before inspection. If you guys want any rubbish burned you'll have to get it up here before then."

"You don't have to worry about that, Fatso," said Judge Jenks. "These Frenchmen have got a racket. They make every ship hire a local barge company to haul their rubbish to sea and dump it.

Now, Hear This!

Even if you've got an incinerator and don't have no rubbish you've gotta pay the barge company anyway, so you might just as well close this place up."

When the *Okinawa* arrived in Nice several days later, Fatso got ashore with the mail orderly in the whirly bird and soon had the Antelope on the phone. She was delighted to hear that Fatso and his great big ship with lots of sailors were back in port. But alas for Fatso and his gang, she was not as delighted as he had predicted she would be. Maids along the waterfront are the same the world over and when a sailor returns from a long voyage they do not always remember the promises they made prior to his sailing. Perhaps the fact that the last time Fatso's ship had been the only one in port may have caused Fatso to exaggerate the impression he had made. Besides, the Antelope had been out with a gunner's mate from the *Iwo Jima* for the last three nights and Fatso's memory had been cooling for one year.

At any rate, when Fatso brought up the 4th of July ball, the Antelope was "Veree sorree, but everybodee ees going with your frands from *Ewo Jeemy.*"

Fatso called all the other numbers in his book and confirmed this bad news. When he got back to the ship and this word spread around, there were ugly mutterings among the crew of the *Okinawa.* Some of the hotheads favored organizing a party to go to the ball, beat up the sailors from the *Iwo Jima* and dismantle the casino, piece by piece. However, for the next couple of days the crew was too busy cleaning up for Admiral "Bread-and-Water" Biggs' inspection to do any detailed planning for this operation.

Getting a ship ready for Admiral's inspection is a big job. It is sort of like spring housecleaning and all sorts of forgotten rubbish and junk from out-of-the-way corners comes to light and has to be disposed of. Ordinarily this would have kept Fatso's big furnace going around the clock but the first day in port a little French tug with a barge in tow came around, collected a large heap of rubbish from the fan tail of the *Okinawa*, and took it many miles to sea and dumped it.

With his furnace shut down, Fatso was able to do an artistic job of getting ready for inspection. He gave the bulkheads and overhead a fresh coat of paint, waxed and polished the linoleum, shined all the bright work till you could see yourself in it, and as a final touch, went over the whole big furnace with stove polish. When he got through, that incinerator compartment was shined up slicker than the inside of a five-inch twin mount.

On the next afternoon, the day before inspection, the little French tug hauled its barge alongside the *Iwo Jima*, took on a load of trash and puffed out of the harbor with its half-filled barge, paying no attention to the frantic blinking of the searchlight on the *Okinawa's* signal bridge. As all seamen know, tug boat captains are unpredictable, and French tug boat captains are the worst of the lot. This one just chugged off and left the *Okinawa* holding quite a sack.

This was the afternoon that Mrs. Worthington's big party was to be held at her villa, situated on the first small cove around the point from the harbor of Nice. Susie referred to this villa as just a sort of "camping-out" place which she occupied during the summer months when her main establishment near Paris was closed. The "little pad" was built of marble with twenty guest rooms and had five acres of gardens around it. The grounds nestled around a little cove opening on the Mediterranean which had been converted into one of the swankiest private swimming beaches in the world.

There were a number of other socialite U.S. tax dodgers besides Susie who had villas along this stretch of the Riviera, some of them with better social ratings than Susie. But the parties which Susie threw at her place made all of them turn green with envy. Susie was dodging a lot more taxes than any of the rest of them so naturally she could heave the biggest parties and attract the most spectacular guests. So the others often forgot they were ladies when you mentioned Susie's name. They referred to her as "The Blaster" because of the gigantic midnight fireworks displays which were a routine feature of any party at her place, even a small dinner for thirty or forty intimate friends. However, the rumor that she had put on a skyrocket display in the graveyard at her fourth husband's funeral was an exaggeration maliciously circulated by her rivals. Actually, the main reason for Susie's fireworks was to let her snooty neighbors know that she was throwing a party to which they had not been invited.

This particular party for Admiral Biggs and the officers from the fleet was to be her crowning effort of the current social season. Millionaires were a dime a dozen, and the principals of every important divorce scandal for the past twenty years were on hand. There were Dukes and Duchesses from every defunct monarchy in Europe, and you couldn't pop a champagne cork without hitting some out-of-work Baron in the monocle.

Susie had outdone herself in planning this party. The midnight fireworks display would be merely incidental this time. The major feature was to be an aquacade in the manner of Billy Rose, with water skiing and fancy diving in the cove right in front of the lawn. This was to be climaxed by a water ballet with a symphony orchestra and brilliant lighting effects from the shore line. There had been much advance publicity and there was no doubt it would be the greatest spectacle ever seen on the Riviera.

That evening Susie, with Admiral Biggs in tow, was all in a flutter over her forthcoming triumph. After a couple of snifters of bourbon, she shifted gears into her Parisian accent and said, "For you, mon gran Amiral, we will make ze greatest display of ze season."

"That reminds me," said the Admiral, who had not yet found out that you didn't talk to Susie at these parties, you just listen, "of the time when—"

Rubbish on the Riviera

"For you, and your great American fleet," continued Susie, "I create new art form—ze water ballet."

"That ought to be good," said the Admiral. "When we were in—"

"It will start as soon as it gets dark," added Susie. "You will be *thrilled.*"

"Last year in Venice I saw—"

"Eet ees a nice breeze which blows in from the sea," observed Susie. "Eet will ruffle the water so eet will be alive and sparkle—non?"

"Umph," grunted the Admiral.

Just before sunset when the party was getting up a pretty good head of steam, a little tug with a barge in tow puffed around the point from Nice and hove to about a half mile off shore and directly up-wind from the entrance to Mrs. Worthington's cove. As Susie had noted, there was a spanking breeze blowing.

The tug was, of course, the one with the rubbish-disposal contract for the fleet. The contract called for taking that stuff way the hell and gone off shore before dumping it. But that very morning the tug boat captain had heard rumors that while he was spending his nights hauling rubbish from the fleet half way across the Mediterranean, his ever-loving sweet patootie had been dating sailors off the *Iwo Jima.* So he had appeared alongside *only* the *Iwo Jima* that afternoon with malice aforethought to create the impression that the coast would be clear. Then, instead of spending the whole night towing his barge to sea, he simply hauled it around the point out of sight from the Port Director's office, dumped it up-wind of Mrs. Worthington's party, and headed back to Nice at four bells and a jingle to check up. Nearly everyone at the party had been too busy getting plastered and swapping gossip about everyone else to pay any attention to the little tug and its barge. Only the Admiral's Flag Lieutenant noticed it in passing, but thought nothing of it at the time.

Now, Hear This!

An hour after sunset the guests all assembled on the lawn to see the great show. At a sign from Susie, a fanfare burst from the orchestra and batteries of colored spotlights on the shore flooded the cove with all the colors of the rainbow and a gasp of delight burst from the spectators. The aquacade was about to begin.

Just at this point the vanguard of the rubbish which the tug had dumped sailed proudly into the cove running free before the wind. Soon an armada of tin cans, empty bottles, broken boxes, and refuse of all sorts invaded the arena for the great spectacle. At first the spectators thought that those sparkling shiny objects on the water were an added lighting effect and waited in titillated suspense for the opening number of the show.

But after an awkward delay, the Frenchman who managed the troop of swimmers came bustling up to Mrs. Worthington in a state of great indignation, announced that he was desolated, and began spouting words about the hazards to his artistes if they attempted to perform among the dangerous obstacles.

By this time Susie had a couple of more jolts of Bourbon under her girdle and was not to be thwarted by small difficulties. If this show were cancelled, after all the advance ballyhoo, it would make her the laughing stock of the Riviera.

"Ze show must go on," she announced with a dramatic wave of her hand.

"Madame—c'est impossible," said the Frenchman.

"Lissen you little twerp," said Susie lapsing back into her native Brooklyn tongue. "Get that goddam ham and egg circus of yours into the cove right now. No show—no pay!"

At this the Frenchman began shouting and gesticulating and said several things in French which Susie did not understand, but took to be insulting. Susie had a pretty good profane vocabulary herself in several languages and nobody was going to call her names in French that she hadn't even heard of before. She grabbed a champagne bottle by the neck and swung it viciously at the man-

106

ager's head.

But he was an agile little Frog and Susie's aim was poor. She missed the manager and bounced the bottle over Admiral Biggs' bald head, throwing the whole place into an uproar. It became necessary to call in the local gendarmes and evict the little manager with all his gorgeous bathing beauties.

As soon as the aquacade had been given the heave-ho, Mrs. Worthington apologized profusely to Admiral Biggs and knocked over a few more hookers of Bourbon to re-steady her nerves. While she was doing this, and the Admiral was graciously assuring her that he didn't mind the clout on the noggin, the butler appeared with a tin can and a piece of driftwood which had been fished out of the cove, both of them bearing the stencilled legend, TO: SUPPLY OFFICER USS IWO JIMA.

The last two hookers of firewater took hold, and Susie cut loose a blast at Admiral Biggs for allowing his fleet to louse up her party. The Admiral, naturally, was burned up about the flagrant disregard of his orders and assured Susie he would take drastic disciplinary action against the offending ship next morning.

On the way back from the party that night, his Flag Lieutenant had to talk fast to convince the Admiral that it really wasn't the *Iwo Jima's* fault at all. He finally persuaded the Admiral not to take any action against the carrier. But whether it was her fault or not, it was certainly her rubbish that had messed up a good party and had embarrassed him, to say nothing of getting him a resounding sock on the gonk. All this tended to prejudice the Admiral against the *Iwo Jima*.

At the same time that the snafu of the party was occurring ashore, a serious crisis had arisen on board the *Okinawa*. When the little tug puffed off with its barge leaving a big pile of rubbish on the fantail of the *Okinawa*, Commissar Jones, in charge of that part of the ship, simply got a five-hand working party, hauled the whole pile forward to the starboard side of the hangar deck, and deposited it outside the incinerator compartment to be burned. Fatso, with his place all shined up for inspection like a new saloon, refused to take cognizance of this rubbish.

"You've *got* to get rid of this stuff," insisted the Commissar. "Inspection is tomorrow morning. There will be hell to pay if it's still here then."

"That's *your* problem, Mac, and I wish you luck with it," said Fatso through the peephole of his barricaded door. "But you ain't going to louse up my place getting rid of it."

"It ain't my problem any more, it's out of *my* part of the ship," observed the Commissar as he shoved off toward the fantail.

In a few minutes an irate hangar-deck officer was hammering on Fatso's door.

"Look, Gioninni," he said. "You can't leave that stuff sitting out here on the hangar deck during inspection. You got to get rid of it."

"But it ain't my stuff, sir," pleaded Fatso. "And the Executive Officer told me I could shut down this furnace till after inspection. I'm all shined up in here now and it will ruin everything if I've got to light off this furnace."

"No matter what anybody told you, you know just as well as I do we've got to get rid of it."

"Couldn't you load it into a motor launch and dump it way out at sea, sir?" asked Fatso desperately.

The hangar-deck officer was also in charge of the ship's motor launches so he vetoed that proposal promptly. "What? And mess up *my* boats for inspection? You get busy and burn that stuff. If you give me any more argument about it, I'll take you to the Exec! I'll get you a sympathy chit from the Chaplain and the key to the weep locker, but *get that stuff burned.*"

Fatso knew he was licked. In a case of this kind, the Exec would certainly side with the Hangar Deck Officer and make him burn the rubbish. But that wouldn't help Fatso any when Admiral Biggs

108

found his place looking like a trash disposal plant at inspection. Fatso could see himself being restricted to the ship by Old Bread-and-Water for a month or more. "Aye aye sir," he said. "Don't bother about seeing the Exec. I'll take care of it."

Fatso's gang were seated around the incinerator while this discussion was going on and had taken it all in.

"Whatcha going to do, Fatso?" asked Beer Bottle after a decent interval.

"I dunno," said Fatso glumly.

"Why not lug it up on the flight deck during the midwatch and leave it up there?" suggested Scuttlebutt, who had a grudge against the flight deck officer.

"That's no good," said Satchelaft scornfully. "Ain't there *someplace* on a ship this size where we could hide it?"

"Naw. They look everywhere at Admiral's inspection," said Judge Jenks.

"If I light off that furnace tonight this place will look like a crap house tomorrow. Old Bread-and-Water will restrict me to the ship and I'll miss the big brannigan when we beat up that *Iwo Jima* mob," said Fatso bitterly.

"But if you don't light it off probably the whole ship will get restricted," said Beer Bottle. "So there won't be no brannigan and the *Iwo Jima* won't get beat up."

Suddenly Fatso's face lit up with an inspiration. "Say-y-y," he said, "I got an idea—I'm just going to heave it overboard."

"That's the one *sure* way of getting the whole ship restricted," observed Judge Jenks. "They're awful strict about that here in Nice. There's a special order out about it."

"Yeah, I know," said Fatso. "That's what makes this particular idea so good. Scuttlebutt, how's to do me a big favor? Jump down to the paint locker and get me half a gallon pot of black paint and a small striping brush. The rest of you guys wait here, I'll be back pretty soon."

Now, Hear This!

"Where you going, Fatso?" demanded Scuttlebutt.

"Down to the print shop," said Fatso enigmatically. "I want to get them to cut me some stencils."

While Fatso was gone there was much speculation as to what he was up to and a few opinions were ventured that he had blown his top. But when he came back with his stencils fifteen minutes later, his scheme became beautifully clear and gleams of admiration lit up all eyes.

The stencils all bore the legend, "TO: SUPPLY OFFICER USS IWO JIMA."

All hands set to work with a will, stencilling this incriminating legend on to each and every piece of rubbish on the Okinawa's hangar deck.

After taps that night the whole rubbish pile disappeared miraculously from outside Fatso's compartment. Some pieces went to the bottom of the harbor and the rest sailed briskly before the breeze until they reached the shore. Sunrise the next morning found the most famous beach in the world littered with rubbish from one end to the other, all of it stencilled "TO: SUPPLY OFFICER USS IWO JIMA."

By eight a.m., a mob of irate hotel managers and beach owners were storming the Mayor's office brandishing pieces of wood bearing the telltale name. The Mayor narrowly escaped lynching because he had made sweeping promises after last year's episode that this could never happen again. Hizzoner clapped on his high silk hat, waddled down to the dock as fast as his short legs would carry him, and chugged out in his official launch to the *Salem* to protest this outrage to Admiral Biggs. By the time he got in to Admiral Biggs' cabin, fire and smoke were blowing out of both his ears and he bitterly denounced the whole American fleet and the *Iwo Jima* in particular.

Signal flags fluttered to the yardarm of the *Salem* and bugles blared on the *Iwo Jima* calling away the Captain's gig on the double. Soon the Captain of the great carrier scrambled up the *Salem*'s gangway, was escorted into the Admiral's cabin all out of breath, and said—"Good morning sir—You sent for me, sir?"

It would be improper to eavesdrop on the next few minutes between the Skipper and Admiral Biggs. Maybe that snafu at Mrs. Worthington's party the night before hadn't been the *Iwo Jima*'s fault, but she was caught with her main sheet belayed this morning. Admiral Biggs told the Captain off in language which the Skipper hadn't had addressed to him since he was an Ensign.

Five minutes later the smarting Skipper scrambled down the gangway of the *Salem*, two steps at a time, jumped into his gig and went boiling back to the *Iwo Jima*. All liberty for the great carrier was cancelled the moment he set foot on board and a large working party of sailors went ashore and spent the rest of the morning cleaning up the beaches.

While they were thus engaged, Admiral Biggs inspected the *Okinawa*. She passed a fine inspection and the Admiral even had a few words of personal approval for her spic-and-span incinerator compartment.

"Looks very well indeed," he said to Fatso. "Do you have any trouble disposing of rubbish here?"

"No indeed, sir," said Fatso. "None whatever, sir, there's a French tug boat comes and gets it every uh—every now and then, sir."

Just before noon that day, as the inspection party was leaving the ship, Fatso's cronies gathered in the incinerator. All hands were congratulating each other on passing a fine inspection.

Suddenly Fatso, who was peering out a port hole yelled, "Hey, *Iwo Jima* is heaving short and getting underway."

As the gang crowded around the port to confirm this development, Judge Jenks came bursting in with hot news.

"The signal bridge intercepted a dispatch from the *Salem* during inspection telling *Iwo Jima* to get underway and proceed

111

to Suda Bay, Crete—She's got to stay there until after Bastille Day."

"Hmmmmm," said Scuttlebutt. "That's the lousiest liberty port in the whole Mediterranean. Must be some trouble brewing in Crete."

"Gangway for a man in a hurry!" yelled Fatso. "I gotta get ashore right away. There's a lot of dames over there that ain't got dates for that 4th of July Ball now."

⚓ CHAPTER SIX

Dog Overboard

THE OKINAWA's great wildcat on the foc'sle ground ponderously around, heaving in the huge anchor chain that held the ship moored in the harbor of Nice. As each link, forged from steel bars as big as a baseball bat, pivoted over the lip of the hawsepipe, a bosun's mate clouted it with a sledge hammer, like the man does in a railroad station to the wheels of the limited after she pulls in.

"What are we doing this for?" inquired a seaman just out of boot camp who had been detailed to help the bosun's mate.

"Every now and then a link goes 'clunk' instead of '*boi-i-i-ng*,' " said the bosun's mate. "Then you know you've got a wormy link."

Two other sailors peering down the hawsepipe squirted high-pressure hoses at the chain emerging from the water to knock the mud and slime off so it wouldn't get on deck.

The Bosun up in the eyes of the ship directing operations kept up a running chatter of orders to the foc'sle gang and reports to the bridge.

"Thirty-five fathoms at the water's edge," he reported as four links painted white and separated by a big shackle emerged from

113

the water.

"Come on, heave around!" bellowed the Bosun at the wildcat man, even though the wildcat operator had his controller on full speed and couldn't do any more. Bosuns are bossy characters who have to holler at somebody.

Then cocking a salty eye over the side he reported, "Chain is up and down, sir" . . . and next, even though the anchor was out of sight twenty fathoms below, "Anchor is breaking groun-n-n-n-d," . . . "ANCHOR'S AWEIGH, SIR."

As he sang out this last report on the battle circuit to the bridge, bugles blew a long blast all over the ship, quartermasters in the bow and stern hauled down the Jack and the big national Ensign, and the smaller set of steaming colors went fluttering up to the gaff just abaft the stack. On the bridge the Captain said, "All engines ahead one-third. Right full rudder. Come right to one-seven-zero."

Two sailors on the engine-room telegraphs swung their brass handles back and forth and stopped them with the pointers on the sector of the dial marked "1/3 Ahead." The engine-room pointer went through similar gyrations, stopped on the same sector, and the revolution indicators came to life.

Both sailors reported rather smugly, as if they were moving the ship themselves, "All engines going ahead one-third, Cap'n."

Meantime, the helmsman flipped his controller to neutral, checking the fifty-ton rudder as his bridge indicator was passing thirty degrees right, and sang out, "Rudder is full right," and then cocking a careful eye at the gyro compass card just jiggling past EAST, "Zero-nine-zero Cap'n, swinging right slowly sir."

The great aircraft carrier *Okinawa* was underway after a two-week visit to Nice, bound for new ports and new adventures. Aboard were 3,000 sailors whose tales about that two week visit would grow in stature as time went on, and left behind were the same varied sentiments and situations that departing ships have been leaving behind them since Columbus' time.

Down in the incinerator compartment an hour later, Fatso was addressing a group of his cronies. "If I never hit the beach in that port again, it will be way too soon."

"What's the matter Fatso?" asked Scuttlebutt. "I thought you had a friend there."

"So did I," said Fatso. "But that little French dame was two-timing me. She had a husband!"

"Oo-la-la," said Beer Bottle. "Spin us the yarn, Fatso."

"Well," said Fatso, "I made a date for the last night we were in port. She had to work till about eight o'clock so I said I'd come around to where she worked and pick her up. At first she didn't want me to, but finally I talked her into it."

"You always did have a way with the gals, Fatso," observed Satchelaft.

"From now on I'll keep my big mouth shut," said Fatso. "The place where she works is about as big as the public library with gardens and parks all around it. There was a whole fleet of limousines parked around it and some kind of a clambake was going on. I went in the back way and met Fifi in a hallway there. We were just doing some preliminary smooching when a wild-eyed Dago cook comes busting out of the galley yelling as if the Germans were coming and waving a carving knife as long as the Captain's sword."

"Golly Fatso! Who was he?"

"He was my little pancake's ever-loving husband. He's the head chef at this joint. Naturally I took off down the hall, but it was a dead-end street, except for a swinging door at the end. I busted through this door and there I was smack in the middle of the swankiest party I've ever not been invited to."

"Don't stop now, Fatso," said Beer Bottle. "Did you give him the slip?"

"Finally I did," said Fatso. "I thought I was safe when I got into this snooty soirée, in a hall half as big as the hangar deck with all those funny-looking dudes and dames standing around juggling tea cups and cookies in the air. Must of been a couple of hundred people there, the women all dressed up like Saturday night at Maime Kelley's, and the men wearing all kinds of foreign uniforms.

"I figured I could just stand around for a while as if I was an orderly or something. But then this wild-eyed Dago chef comes busting out of the hallway waving his cleaver and I had to scram."

"What happened then Fatso?" asked Satchelaft eagerly.

"I laid a course for the main exit," said Fatso. "And bent on a flock of knots. There was a couple of fat battle-axes in my way and I guess maybe I jostled one or two of them a bit as I went by but—but I got out. Caught the nine o'clock boat back to the ship . . . and I guess that's the end of that."

"That's what *you* think Fatso," said Beer Bottle gravely. "Don't you know what that joint was where you got the bum's rush? It was the official residence of the Prefect General, and the party you crashed was a big annual event. I hear you knocked Madame Le Prefect smack on her can. There's a big stink about it in town this morning."

"Gee," said Fatso.

At this point all hands looked at each other as the heartbeat of the ship from the main engines suddenly stopped. The general alarm clanged, there was a shrill blast of the bosun's pipe over the PA system and word rang through the ship, "Man overboard! Starboard side."

You don't stop to ask questions when they pass *that* word. You get up on deck and do what you can for the guy in the water, because maybe you will be in his shoes some day.

All of Fatso's gang came tumbling out of the incinerator just as the bugle was blaring "Assembly." On the end of the bugle call came the announcement, "Now Hear This. This is a drill.

This is a drill." But all hands continued on the double to their muster stations, including even Fatso.

Fatso enjoyed many unofficial prerogatives on this ship and never had to attend any muster personally—except in the case of man overboard. Then, you have to get a complete and accurate muster as soon as possible to make sure it isn't a false alarm and that somebody really is in the drink, and also to find out who the guy was in case you don't get him back.

On the bridge, the Captain stood in the background observing the OOD with a critical eye and let the young officer run the show. As soon as the ship, with engines stopped, had coasted far enough so that the stern was clear of the dummy they had heaved overboard and the "man" could not be caught in the screws, the OOD barked, "All engines ahead standard speed." The rudder was already hard over right to swing the stern away from the man and also to make a full circle and stop the ship near the man. It is usually quicker by several minutes to do this than to back her down, stop half a mile or so away, and send a boat back. Unless of course you have a helicopter, in which case you don't even have to stop at all.

Dozens of extra lookouts were already clambering aloft to keep the "man" in sight and down in CIC the officer of the watch had leaped to the Dead Reckoning Tracer the instant the word was passed and had made a mark on the trace. The DRT is a little mechanical bug hooked up to the gyro compass and the main shafts so that it creeps across a plotting sheet, drawing an accurate track of the ship through the water. If the lookouts lose sight of a man at night, the CIC officer can conn the ship back to the spot where he went overboard by just coaching the bridge until they bring the bug back to the "X" he has made.

A series of coughing explosions down on the flight deck indicated that they were starting the helicopter. "Secure the whirlybird," the Captain said. "This is supposed to be night time. And besides, I want to see if this bucket can still lower a boat."

As the ship heeled to port and swung into a tight turn to starboard, the OOD barked, "Call away number one motor whaleboat."

The bosun's mates and bugles relayed this word through the ship and soon #1 MWB, nestling under the overhang of the flight deck fifty feet above the water, reported "Manned and ready."

The coxswain of this whaleboat was none other than our friend Scuttlebutt and the engineer was Beer Bottle Bates.

"Fatso's in a worse jam than he thinks this time," observed Scuttlebutt as he shipped the plug in the whaleboat. "You guys on the boat falls work fast when we hit the water," he barked at the boat's crew.

"Yeah," said Beer Bottle, priming his engine and wrapping the starting lanyard around the flywheel. "His ass is really in a bight. He's going to need all the drag he's got with the Old Man and Exec to get out of this one."

"I hope he makes it," said Scuttlebutt, shipping the steering oar. As the ship trembled from backing of the screws when she neared the "man" he yelled, "Hey you on that sea painter in the bow. Don't watch nothing but me when we hit the water, and when I tell you to pull that toggle, GET IT OUT OF THERE. Okay boys, Stand by."

On deck the Bosun hollered, "Lower away together on both falls." . . . "*Get your foot out of that bight of line*, YOU ————— ————— LANDLUBBER," . . . "Easy in the forward fall—don't spill 'em in the water," etc., etc., yelling all the usual things a bosun does when he's trying to lower a boat fifty feet on an even keel from a rolling ship into a heavy swell.

At just the right instant he bellowed "UP BEHIND!" and the men at the davits flipped the boat falls off the cleats, letting them run free and dropping the boat the last three feet as level as a billiard table just as a swell came up to meet it.

The lad in the bow got his big block unhooked with one yank of his lanyard, and the boys on deck snatched it clear so it couldn't flog around and brain somebody in the boat. The hook on the after block jammed in the shackle and Scuttlebutt dove at it with a blast of seafaring language and wrenched it clear in utter disregard of the danger of losing a handful of fingers as the big block thrashed around.

Regaining his feet Scuttlebutt grabbed the steering oar and sheared the boat out from the side of the ship, keeping an even strain on the sea painter as Beer Bottle started his engine.

"Cast off!" yelled Scuttlebutt. "Get that —— —— —— toggle pin out," indicating tersely and graphically that the ancestry of that particular toggle pin had been most remarkable.

In a few minutes Scuttlebutt had the dummy in the boat, the boat was hoisted back aboard, the *Okinawa* resumed her course and speed, and life settled back to normal again.

Normal, that is, for everybody but Fatso. The last mail from the beach before getting underway that morning contained an official letter from Monsieur Le Prefect to the Admiral. It protested about United States Navy sailors barging around his main salon like battering rams when he was trying to throw a party, scoring spares and strikes among his guests and upsetting applecarts and dowagers all over the place. Monsieur Le Prefect took a dim view of the matter, and said so in somewhat undiplomatic language. But worst of all, his gendarmes had obviously put the squeeze on Fifi, because the latter had fingered John Patrick Gioninni, BM1c, U.S.S. *Okinawa*, as the perpetrator of this insult to the honor of la belle France.

Fatso, having an in with the Chief Yeoman who opened the Admiral's mail, naturally knew the contents of this letter before the Admiral did. But that didn't help any. It had come aboard registered so Fatso's first idea of just dropping it over the side was out.

In desperation Fatso hunted up "Commissar" Jones. Usually Fatso avoided Commissar as he would a rattlesnake with the measles but he hoped that Commissar *might* inadvertently be useful to him now.

"Hi ya, Jonesy," said Fatso, "Have a good time in Nice?"

"Pretty good," admitted Jonesy warily. "What do *you* want now?"

"Jonesy," said Fatso, "you remember seeing me here on the hangar deck last night, don't you?"

"Yeah," said Jones, "about eleven o'clock—right after six bells went."

"No, I mean the *other* time," said Fatso. "Don't you remember about *eight o'clock*—right after the watch changed?"

Jones looked rather sharply at Fatso. "No-o-o, I don't," he said. "Matter of fact, I don't see how you could of been aboard at eight o'clock when I *seen* you go ashore in the seven o'clock boat and come back in the nine o'clock."

"Now wait a minute, Jonesy," said Fatso. "You got me mixed up with that chubby first-class cook down in the galley. This is important. See if you can't remember, pal."

"I remember perfectly," said Jones, "and I remember a lot of other stuff you've pulled on me since we've been on this bucket together. I ain't good enough for you and your gang am I? Well— I ain't furnishing you no phony alibi, sailor," he sneered. "And from what I hear, you really need one this time. You'll get no help from me, Mr. Gioninni—all of my shipmates went down on the *Maine*."

There was no use heaving in on that line any further.

That night when Fatso's gang gathered down in the incinerator compartment for their regular evening meeting the usual carefree atmosphere of these soirées was missing, as all hands racked their brains for some way to get Fatso off the hook.

Scuttlebutt, having been busted twice by summary courts-martial, was a recognized expert on legal matters. "They won't give you no court, Fatso," he opined. "It would be too complicated. We won't be nowheres near Nice for the next six months. You are the only one on this ship who was there when it happened and they can't make you testify against yourself. If that dumb Ensign who defended me the last time hadn't advised me to take the witness stand, I'll bet I'd still be first class. So, if you just keep your mouth shut, the only way they could get any witnesses against you would be to ship a whole barge load of fat-assed duchesses halfway across Europe—and they ain't gonna do that."

"That's right," agreed Beer Bottle. "The *Salem* is shoving off for South Africa next week right after we join up with her. I'll bet we could stall this thing off for a week easy, get you transferred to her, and then they'd never catch up with you."

"Nothing doing," said Fatso. "I'd rather be a swab jockey on this bucket than a chief on that madhouse."

Grave nods all around the circle confirmed Fatso's estimate of the relative merits of these two rival ships.

At this point there was a scratching on the watertight door leading in to the incinerator. "Open the door, Satchelaft," said Fatso, "and let Hawsepipe in."

Hawsepipe, a brown and white wire-haired terrier, came bounding in wagging his whole stern end, went dutifully around the circle putting his paws up on each one and receiving a friendly pat, and wound up jumping into Fatso's lap to lick his face.

Hawsepipe was the Admiral's dog, had been going to sea with him for ten years and, in the Admiral's opinion, he was the best dog on any ship in the ocean. Naturally he had the run of the ship, and being a smart little dog who had lived in a dozen other ships, he soon knew his way around the great carrier better than half the sailors in her. It hadn't taken him long to discover that Fatso's place was where the best people on the ship hung out, and that right after four bells of the evening watch he could always get a wonderful bone down there. So when the Admiral retired to his sea cabin at night, Hawsepipe usually dropped down to Fatso's place.

Fatso tossed Hawsepipe a big steak bone with plenty of meat left on it and Hawsepipe settled down in his regular corner to gnaw on the bone, with one ear cocked to the conversation.

"Too bad that letter came to the Admiral instead of the Captain," observed Scuttlebutt.

"Yeah," said Fatso, "I could fix this rap with the Old Man easy. I swum around holding him up for a couple of hours after the *Lexington* got sunk and he's been kind of friendly toward me ever since."

"How about the Admiral. He's an old timer. You must know him too, Fatso."

"Only by reputation," said Fatso. "And he's supposed to be a crusty old buzzard. Never saw him before he came aboard here a couple of months ago."

"Nice dog he's got," said Beer Bottle. "He can't be such a bad guy."

"All right now. Never mind about the Admiral's dog," said Satchelaft. "We got a serious problem to work on here. This one is a little different from the usual beef that comes up after we leave a European port. Take that riot in Naples—there were a few Eyetalians got hurt, there were some windows got busted, and those two street cars got pushed off the track and rolled down the hill into the bay. The Eyetalian government demanded a million bales of liras for damages, and we were suckers enough to give it to them."

"Yeah," said Beer Bottle. "And the whole thing was started by that Dago cab driver. We never should of paid them a cent."

"Anyway," continued Satchelaft, "I suppose they figured they had to lower the boom on a few of our guys because it cost the

122

government so much dough. But this is different. It isn't going to cost Uncle Sugar a cent. The Frenchmen have got their feathers ruffled but all they want is an apologetic letter from the Admiral to redeem ze honneur of la France."

"That's right," said Fatso. "But admirals get sore when they have to write apologetic letters. And then they get out their big black whip and go to work on the guy who caused it."

"He's going to have to write the letter—no doubt about that," said Satchelaft. "But can't you get the Captain to go to bat for you and get the Admiral to just sweep the rest of it under the rug after he writes the letter?"

"I wouldn't ask the Captain to put himself on the spot for me that way with the Admiral."

There was a long pause after which Satchelaft said, "You know, we've all got a big drag with a very close friend of the Admiral's."

"Whaddaya mean?" demanded several voices.

"Hawsepipe here is a friend of ours, and the Admiral thinks more of him than he does of another star."

"Yabbut what's that got to do with the NATO Alliance?" demanded Fatso.

"Keep your flat hat on and maybe you'll find out—you used to be a frogman didn't you, Fatso?"

"Sure. I hit all the beaches at Iwo Jima clearing out mines twenty-four hours before most of the guys who are bragging to their kids now that they were in the first assault wave."

"Can you still handle yourself in the water?" asked Satchelaft.

"Who? *Me??* Why I can still pass the frogman test wearing dress blues and leggings, carrying a rifle, and—"

"Okay, okay. Would you mind going overboard at night in smooth water if you knew they'd spot you right away?"

"Not if you lugs in the whaleboat didn't foul up the deal," said Fatso looking at Scuttlebutt and Beer Bottle. "What are you leading up to anyway?"

Now, Hear This!

"Fatso," said Satchelaft, "you're in bad trouble with the Admiral, and we all know that Hawsepipe has a big drag with the Admiral. Now suppose the Admiral thought you had rescued Hawsepipe from drownding. I'll bet he'd forget about that deal back at Nice."

"Wait a minute," said Fatso. "If you're suggesting that we heave Hawsepipe overboard so I can rescue him—just forget it. Why I wouldn't do that to . . . to . . . not even to Commissar Jones."

Hawsepipe jammed his bone into a corner where he could get a little better purchase on it, growled a bit at it, and gnawed away.

"Don't go jumping to conclusions, Fatso," said Satchelaft. "I wouldn't heave Hawsepipe overboard either. I just said suppose the Admiral *thought* he went over the side and that you saved him. That would be good—wouldn't it?"

By now everybody except Hawsepipe was hanging on Satchelaft's words, suspense and interest shining from every face.

"Go ahead," said Fatso. "What's the pitch?"

"Suppose Scuttlebutt here takes Hawsepipe up and hides him in the motor whaleboat. You and I go back aft on the fantail and wait till there's nobody around. Then I dial the bridge on the ship's phone and pass the word, "Man overboard, starboard side." I'll start hollering as loud as I can and as soon as they pull the general alarm, so we know for sure the bridge has the word, over the side you go Fatso. I'll let go the Franklin life buoy, heave over a couple of flares, and all you've got to do is float around and take it easy till Scuttlebutt comes back and gets you in the whaleboat. You can even wear a Mae West if you want to."

"I wouldn't be found dead wearing one of them things," snorted Fatso.

"Anyway," continued Satchelaft, "while all this commotion is going on, we start the word around that Hawsepipe fell overboard and somebody jumped in after him. Pretty soon Scuttlebutt comes along in the whaleboat with Hawsepipe in it, and fishes you out of the water. On the way back to the ship you dunk Hawsepipe to get him wet and when you bring him up to the bridge and give him to the Admiral, I think we'll have this job made."

Around the circle of Fatso's cronies unqualified approval beamed from all faces. Hawsepipe just turned his bone over, growled a little bit and gnawed away.

"Yabbut how about Hawsepipe?" asked Fatso. "You may have trouble with him in the boat. He might get excited at all the noise and start jumping around."

"No he won't," said Satchelaft. "Why, that dog has got almost as much sea duty as you have, Fatso. He's used to riding in boats. The Admiral takes him ashore on liberty in the barge with him everywhere we go. We'll give him a new bone to keep him quiet and I'll stow him under that tarpaulin in the stern sheets till we get clear of the side."

Satchelaft reached over to scratch Hawsepipe's ears, and Hawsepipe quit gnawing for a minute and let out a friendly routine growl—meaning, "How's to leave me alone for a while, sailor, I'm busy."

Fatso and his gang were not the kind to diddle around indecisively once a plan of action had been decided. Hawsepipe was provided with a luscious new bone, and Scuttlebutt lugged him up to the whaleboat and deposited him in the stern sheets where he settled down to work on the new bone.

Fatso and Satchelaft adjourned to the fantail carrying a weighted bundle of rags about the size of Hawsepipe. This was an afterthought in case some nosey guy happened to be standing at the ramp on the flight deck watching the wake, as people often do at night. The bundle of rags would make a splash about the same size as Hawsepipe would have.

Satchelaft dialed the bridge and said very clearly and distinctly to the man who answered, "Man overboard, starboard side—*Man overboard.*" Allowing a few seconds for this news to sink in, **Fatso** heaved the bundle of rags over and then he and Satchelaft began bellowing, "Man overboard, Man overboard!" On the second bellow the first clang of the general alarm sounded and Fatso did a clean jackknife dive into the boiling wake.

Satchelaft released the big copper life buoy with the magnesium flares on it, and as they lit up he saw Fatso swimming an easy crawl stroke only a few yards from the buoy as the engines stopped, the rudder went over, and the ship swung into her turn.

Soon the fantail was jammed with rubbernecks (who should have been in ranks mustering). Satchelaft planted a rumor among them that the Admiral's dog had fallen overboard, some guy had jumped overboard after him, and then beat it up to his mustering station.

In less time than it takes to tell, this rumor was down in the engine rooms and up on the signal bridge. A rural party line isn't even in the same league with a big naval ship when it comes to spreading rumors.

The Admiral had just stepped out of his sea cabin and was standing alongside the Captain peering aft at the flares bobbing in the water astern. He got the rumor about Hawsepipe a few seconds after Satchelaft started it. He whirled around and yelled, "Orderly! Go see if you can find Hawsepipe around the main cabin."

The Marine Corporal banged his heels together, saluted, said, "Aye aye sir," and dashed off.

Then, after a brief interval torn between duty and sentiment, the Admiral said to the Captain rather plaintively, "Captain, you're not doing all this just for my little dog, are you?"

"The word I got was man overboard, Sir," said the Captain. "And I'm proceeding on that basis. Matter of fact, I would do it for your dog, Sir, or anybody else's dog, for that matter."

126

The Admiral did not seem inclined to make an issue of the matter at this point.

"And besides," said the Captain, "it's a darned good drill even if it is Hawsepipe"—thus clinching the easiest victory he had ever won in an argument with an Admiral.

Everything clicked even better that night than it had in the morning. Within five minutes Scuttlebutt had hauled Fatso into the whaleboat and was towing the big lifebuoy back to the ship.

It almost broke up a beautiful friendship when Fatso reached under the tarpaulin, heaved Hawsepipe's bone overboard, grabbed him by the collar, dunked him over the side and dragged him aboard again. Hawsepipe bounced around all over the boat yapping at the top of his lungs and demanding his bone back from all hands in the boat's crew. Thus the Admiral knew long before the boat was hoisted back aboard that his little dog was safe.

As Fatso climbed out of the boat and started along the hangar deck toward the bridge ladder with Hawsepipe under his arm, Commissar Jones fell in step alongside him.

"Well, well, well," said Commissar. "Mister Hero himself!"

Fatso's reply could not be repeated in Sunday School class.

"Don't get tough with me, smarty-pants," warned Commissar. "I'm wise to this whole phony deal tonight, and I'll be around in the morning to see what we're going to do about it." On that ominous note Commissar shoved off.

Fatso knew that a slight touch of blackmail would be all in a day's work for Commissar—but it was too late now to back out.

The Admiral was touched when Fatso came up the bridge dripping wet with Hawsepipe in his arms and delivered the little dog to him. Even the quartermasters, signalmen, and strikers choked up a little at this human interest scene. Hawsepipe was the only one who took it all in stride, shaking himself vigorously and throwing salt water all over the Admiral and Captain.

Now, Hear This!

"Son," said the Admiral, addressing Fatso, "do you mean to tell me you jumped overboard on a dark night, with the ship making fifteen knots, just to—"

"Aw, it was nothin' sir," interrupted Fatso modestly.

"Well I'm certainly grateful to you for saving my little dog," said the Admiral. "We've been together a long time."

"By the way Admiral," said the Captain. "This is Gioninni, that man you were speaking to me about this afternoon."

"So-o-o-o?" said the Admiral. "Well, all I can say is he can't be anywhere near as bad a chap as those crazy Frenchmen claim . . . Look, Cap'n, I'll take care of that matter. You just forget what I told you this afternoon."

"Aye Aye Sir," said the Captain.

"By the way, Gioninni," said the Admiral, "you must have seen this happen. How did Hawsepipe happen to go overboard in the first place?"

"Well Sir," said Fatso, "I'd rather not say."

"Why not?" demanded the Admiral. "Hawsepipe is a good sailor. He knows his way round aboard ship. I want to know what happened."

"Admiral," said Fatso, "I don't know the name of the guy who done it, and I couldn't identify him if I saw him. But Hawsepipe was just sitting there at the stern minding his own business and watching the wake, when this big angular black-haired guy came up behind him, hauled off and kicked him smack overboard. I think this guy had a badge on his chest—sort of like some of the masters-at-arms wear."

While the Captain and Admiral gaped at each other in horror and amazement, Fatso saluted respectfully and shoved off for the incinerator, knowing full well that any tall angular black haired guy on the master-at-arms force who tried to tell the Captain or Admiral derogatory stories about Fatso Gioninni would find himself with his neck in a bight.

Dog Overboard

The grapevine had Fatso's version of the story of how Hawse-pipe fell overboard all over the ship in a matter of minutes, and Commissar Jones decided on second thought that trying to black-mail a shipmate would not be a nice thing to do.

⚓ CHAPTER SEVEN

Fatso's Miracle

As THE OKINAWA swung into the wind to launch a squadron of jet fighter planes, a riot of systematic confusion and careful haste broke out on her flight deck. Several dozen jet engines lit off with a deafening roar, and the catapult crews, performing with acrobatic precision, flung the first four planes into the air at fifteen-second intervals.

As the fifth plane leaped forward along the catapult track and crossed the bow, the scream of the crash siren cut through the thunder of engines and all heads on the flight deck snapped forward to see what was wrong.

The towing bridle had broken halfway down the catapult track, and #5 got a "slow" shot—rolling off the bow at only 80 knots, not enough speed to stay in the air. The pilot did everything possible. He flipped his wheels up the instant he went over the ramp, he nosed over slightly to use the 70-foot altitude of the flight deck trying to pick up speed, and then held her off to the last possible second nursing the nose-up while his wide-open jets struggled against the drag and inertia to accelerate the plane to flying speed. But it couldn't be done. A hundred yards ahead of

130

the ship she stalled out and crashed into the water, leaving half the tail sticking out when the splash subsided.

The seconds dragged by while all hands watched tensely for a head to bob up in the water alongside the slowly sinking tail. None appeared.

On the bridge the Captain barked, "Right full rudder, stop port engines . . ." swerving the ship to avoid running down the crash or sucking it into the screws. A few seconds later he ordered "Left full rudder—come back to launching course."

The rescue helicopter, always poised a few hundred feet off the starboard side when launching, nosed over and beat the air furiously as it sped toward the crash. Before the *Okinawa* got back on course, the pilot horsed back on the stick and hovered the "angel" smack over the crash 20 feet from the water.

His crew man, Web Foot Foley, was already dangling over the side in the big horse-collar sling suspended from the helicopter's electric winch. Holding the whirly bird in exact position with one hand the pilot hit the "lowering" control of the winch with the other, and Foley plummeted down and disappeared under water. Soon the winch was grinding cable back in again and presently the horse collar emerged from the water with Web Foot bearing a limp figure in his arms.

Two minutes after the crash #6 plane roared off the catapult as the whirly bird was depositing the stunned but uninjured pilot on deck. You can easily see why the pilots all affectionately refer to the whirly bird as the "angel."

That night after taps, Fatso was presiding over the regular nightly gathering of his cronies. They were discussing the cutter race between the *Okinawa* and her sister ship *Iwo Jima*, to be held when the two ships met in Palermo next week. These ships were bitter rivals in everything from catapult-launching intervals to crap shooting, and each one had a cutter crew that had beaten the best boats the French, British, and Italian Navies had been able to put against them. Naturally, both ships were collecting some money to bet on the forthcoming race between their two undefeated boats.

"How much you got in the pot now, Fatso?" asked Beer Bottle.

"2,640 bucks," replied Fatso. "And the way it's rolling in every day we'll have over ten thousand by next week."

"I hear they'll cover any amount we can raise," observed Beer Bottle. "They say there's a Reserve Ensign over there whose old man owns a whole squadron of banks, and he'll toss in anything they need to cover us up to ten grand."

"Boy! A pot that size will give us a nice cut for our slush fund," observed Scuttlebutt. He was referring to the small fee which the inner sanctum crowd charged for the many public services they rendered in connection with betting pools on the *Okinawa*. They collected the money, conducted all negotiations about placing it, handled the payoff afterwards, and in addition, before paying off, they changed the money at a bank ashore into the local currency of the port where the ship happened to be. Paying off in francs, liras, or piasters, as the case might be, saved trouble and delay for the happy sailors when they went ashore on liberty to celebrate.

The only thing the inner sanctum got for all these services was the "breakage," which is, of course, a legitimate fee recognized by members of the sporting fraternity the world over. However, the way Fatso and his people figured breakage would cause any bookie or track operator to drool with envy. In Italy, for instance, the smallest note they used in paying off was 50 lira, the odd lira between 1 and 49 going into the breakage fund. This usually worked out to be between 3 and 4 per cent of the total pot, which isn't much, of course, considering overhead. And when your overhead consists of such items as Fatso, Beer Bottle, Scuttlebutt, and the rest of their cronies, you've got something to consider.

"What's the latest dope on their boat?" asked Fatso of Satchelaft, coxswain of the *Okinawa*'s cutter crew.

Fatso's Miracle

"They beat that Limey crew in Malta by a length and a half last week," replied Satchelaft, "exactly the same as we did."

"This'll be a honey of a race," observed Beer Bottle. "Almost a dead heat—a good even money bet."

"Yabbut you'll never build up a fund to retire on by laying heavy dough on even-money propositions," said Fatso philosophically.

"Aw, we'll give 'em our wash all the way," said Satchelaft. "Their coxswain won't see nothin' but the seat of my pants after the race starts—it's just like money from home."

At this point Web Foot Foley, a charter member of the inner sanctum, entered—and the race was forgotten momentarily while all hands complimented him on his fine rescue job that morning.

"It wasn't nothin' much," said Web Foot modestly. "After swimmin' around those Philippine beaches during the war pulling detonators out of mines on the bottom, this here whirly bird job is practically a boondoggle."

"Have any trouble getting him out?" inquired Fatso.

"Nope. He didn't even have his shoulder harness buckled."

"That was a break for you, wasn't it?"

"Hunh!" snorted Web Foot. "If the dumb cluck had had it buckled he wouldn't of been knocked out in the first place, and I wouldn't of had to ruin a good pair of shoes going down after him and dragging him out—I dunno what these dizzy fly boys would do if they didn't have guys like me to be their guardian angel."

"You still keep your hand in at that Frogman stuff don't you?" asked Fatso, who had been a Frogman himself during the war.

"I sure do—I've got the full outfit, hand paddles, web feet and breathing helmet—I swim clear under the ship with it every day that we're in port."

"Any barnacles on the ship's bottom now?" asked Fatso.

"Plenty of 'em. I'll bet they slow us down a couple of knots."

"That's right," said Scuttlebutt. "I'm standing throttle watches in the engine room now, and to make twenty knots we gotta make turns for twenty-two."

"Hmmmmm!" said Fatso. "A couple of knots on a big ship like this from barnacles! Well whaddaya know about that?"

Nobody in the crowd seemed to know much about it, or to care either. But they all knew that when Fatso said "Hmmmmm," with that particular inflection, something was cooking inside that crafty head of his—something usually worthwhile, and often worth money. So, they all maintained a respectful silence.

"What kind of shape are you in now, Web Foot?" asked Fatso. "I mean, how long can you stay under water and how far can you swim?"

"Oh—half an hour and a couple of miles," said Web Foot.

Fatso lapsed into deep thought and for a while the discussion branched into other channels. Finally Fatso remarked to no one in particular,

"Wouldn't it be a good break for us if the *Iwo Jima*'s cutter had a lot of barnacles on its bottom the day of the race?"

"Sure," said Beer Bottle. "And it would also be good if all their oars busted right after the race started—or if they forgot to heave in their anchor."

Fatso ignored the sarcasm. "How much dough have you got in the pool on this race, Web Foot?"

"Fifty bucks."

"Would you like to bet some more if you were *sure* we'd win?"

"Well now, of course when I'm *sure* I'm gonna win I always bet all I can get ahold of. But since I lost that pair of loaded dice I used to trim the Limeys with, I ain't had no *sure* propositions."

By this time all hands were following the discussion with great interest. Fatso never came directly to the point in cases of this kind. But it was obvious he was leading up to something and they knew from past experience it would be something pretty good.

"Suppose," said Fatso, "one of them racing cutters had a bunch of little rubber suction cups stuck on its bottom like barnacles— those things about the size of quarters that they put on the windshields of automobiles, and suppose they had little pieces of wire sticking out of them into the water. How much do you think that would slow a cutter down in a two-mile race?"

"Oh, I dunno," said Web Foot. "Maybe a couple of 'em would amount to one length—what has that got to do with global strategy?"

"Well," said Fatso, "if we stuck about a dozen of them on the bottom of the *Iwo Jima's* boat just before the race, that would slow her down about six lengths, wouldn't it?"

"Yeah—but if we stuck a limpet mine on, that would be even better except that some nosey guys might get suspicious when the boat blew up. How could you get away with it? Both boats have to hoist out and weigh in on the *Iwo Jima* just before the race, and each boat gets inspected with a microscope—you couldn't possibly . . ."

"Well now," said Fatso, "It all depends on how you go about it. You can't just walk up while the boat is hoisted out and say, 'How's to look the other way while I stick these things on the bottom.' But if you were sort of careful about it, and had a real good Frogman swimming around under water while the boats were waiting at the starting line . . ."

Eyes popped all around the circle, and gleams of admiration lit up.

"The guy's a genius," breathed Beer Bottle.

"Greatest naval strategist since Halsey," observed Judge Jenks.

"Strike me cross-eyed and bowlegged," said Web Foot. "I could do it with one hand tied behind me."

"Wait a minute," objected the Marine Top Sergeant. "We could win the race that way all right. But the minute they hoisted their boat out afterwards they'd find out, and there would be hell

Now, Hear This!

to pay. They would protest the race and get their money back."

"There'd be hell to pay all right," said Fatso. "But they couldn't get their money back. A protest has to be made within five minutes of the finish. Otherwise the result is final and that's that. This whole betting pool has got to be under cover, so you'd never get either Captain to take any official action. And besides, we always draw up a written agreement signed by both parties and give it to the stake-holder. The official rules of the race are made part of this agreement and there ain't a word in those rules about sticking suction cups on the other guy's boat."

"That's right," agreed Judge Jenks, who was one of the legal experts of the crowd. "And then too, there's nothing in the rules to prevent the other guy from pulling them off after we put them on . . . I can't see a thing wrong with the deal *legally*."

So plans went forward on that basis. In the next couple of days everybody in the inner sanctum stretched their credit to the limit, drew all the money they had on the books, and bet their shirts on the race.

On the day of the race, the *Okinawa* and the *Iwo Jima* lay anchored a half a mile apart off Palermo. That morning the *Okinawa's* cutter was towed over to the *Iwo Jima* where the weighing-in and final inspection of the boat by the judges of the race, the opposing coxswain, and other interested parties took place. Fatso went over in the motor launch that towed the cutter, accompanied by a delegation from the crew, including Beer Bottle. He wore a money belt containing ten one-thousand-dollar bills obtained that morning from the Paymaster in exchange for smaller currency, together with a government check for $75.00, payable to St. Anne's Orphanage, Brooklyn, New York.

The *Okinawa's* delegation was met at the gangway by a similar one on the *Iwo Jima*, headed by Brizlinski, Chief Gunner's Mate, who was Fatso's opposite number on the *Iwo Jima*. Brizlinski also wore a money belt containing $10,000.

136

Fatso's Miracle

The delegations immediately repaired to the incinerator for the process of placing the money in escrow. Fatso and Brizlinski unbuckled their money belts and the ten one-thousand-dollar bills in each were carefully counted. The twenty grand notes were placed in another belt, on which the money pocket was then securely buckled up. Large gobs of sealing wax were melted over each of the two buckles, and two additional gobs were melted over the flap of the pocket. Brizlinski put his thumb print on the seal over one buckle, Fatso on the other, and one representative from each ship put his on the flap seals. There were five reliable witnesses to this ritual from each ship who could testify that everything was on the up and up.

Fatso and Brizlinski then proceeded with the sealed belt to the office of Father O'Brien, Lieutenant Commander, USN, Chaplain of the *Iwo Jima,* who had been selected to be stake-holder. Father O'Brien was well known to all hands in the crews of both ships as a completely reliable character with wide experience in transactions of this kind.

"Good morning me lads," said Father O'Brien, "And what spiritual problem brings the pair of you down here this fine morning?"

"It's the boat race, Father. The boys want to put up a—trophy —for the winner, and we'd like to have you hold it for us till the race is over and then give it to the winner. This here is Fatso Gioninni, Father, the *Okinawa*'s representative."

"Sure, I've known Fatso ever since he was a boot seaman. How are you, Fatso?"

"I'm fine, Father," said Fatso. "And, Father, here's a little check the boys on the ship would like to have you send in for them to St. Anne's Orphanage."

"And here's another from the *Iwo,*" said Brizlinski.

"My! My! $150.00 dollars, that's a nice little sum. I'm sure the good sisters will be pleased with this. They will send many prayers up to heaven for the boys," said the Padre, as he pocketed the two checks. "And now, I suppose you have the agreements about the conditions of this award?"

"Yes Father, here's your copy," said Brizlinski.

Father O'Brien scanned the articles, noted that they were in due form, and gave each of the principals a receipt for the trophy.

"The judges' boat leaves the ship at 1030," said Brizlinski. "And we have permission to ride in it. According to that there agreement the trophy will be turned over to me or Fatso on the judges' boat as soon as the official decision is announced."

"I understand," said Father O'Brien. "I'll be on the judges' boat."

At 1045, the two cutters were lowered into the water and the crews paddled leisurely to the starting line. The two-mile course was clearly marked with buoys, and hundreds of gaily decorated yachts were anchored well back from the fairway along both sides of the course. Harbor police and naval picket boats patrolled the area to shoo off fishing boats and tugs with barges in tow while the race was in progress. A flotilla of several dozen motor boats loaded with sailors from the *Okinawa* and *Iwo Jima* stood by behind the starting line to follow the race and cheer their crews.

As the two racing cutters neared the starting line and lay to about 20 yards apart to wait for the five-minute "stand by" signal, a motor whaleboat from the *Okinawa* cruised slowly around about 50 yards away. This boat was manned by three members of Fatso's inner sanctum, Judge Jenks being the coxswain, Scuttlebutt the engineer, and Web Foot Foley the bow hook. Web Foot made a queer-looking bow hook in his frogman's outfit, so he kept down and out of sight. No one else was in this boat because all military men know from long experience that the only way to keep any operation top secret is to confine knowledge of it to those "who need to know."

A few minutes before the "stand by" signal went up, Web Foot took careful bearings on the two cutters, put on his helmet, slipped over the side, and swam toward the *Iwo Jima*'s boat with a handful of suction cups.

Now, ordinarily, swimming under water to a spot 50 yards away would have been child's play for Web Foot. But, on this particular morning, the wind and tide were running against each other. The tide tended to carry the boats sideways across the course to the south, while the wind tended to blow them to the north. The result of the opposing forces was that the boats stood still.

But Web Foot, swimming under water, was affected only by the tide and he wound up under the *Okinawa*'s boat instead of the *Iwo Jima*'s! He skillfully fastened eight suction cups to *his own* boat and swam back away from the starting line, unseen by anybody.

At 1115 the "stand by" signal went up and the cutters eased slowly up to the starting line. With the two boats poised exactly on the line the starter fired his gun, and they were off to a perfect start. But that's about the only thing that was perfect about the whole race from there on. At the end of the starting sprint, *Iwo Jima* was half a length in front and when the crews settled down to their regular racing beat she seemed to gain about six inches on every stroke. Jubilant howls from the *Iwo Jima* rooters rent the air and the *Okinawa* sailors frantically urged their boys to pull harder.

At the one-mile marker *Iwo Jima* had opened up a lead of five lengths open water, and any experienced horse player would have termed this event a "boat race" in more ways than one. *Okinawa*'s powerful crew was rowing beautifully, but despite a thirty-eight beat, bending the oars as if to break them, and if anything, pulling better than *Iwo Jima*, they weren't going as fast!

On the judges' boat, Fatso was stunned at this unbelievable turn of events. As they neared the three quarter mark he shook his head and muttered, "Holy catfish! These guys are the world's

Now, Hear This!

champs—what would they do with a clean bottom? Maybe something happened and Web Foot couldn't get the gimmicks on."

Half a mile from the finish line it had become a runaway with *Okinawa* ten lengths behind. But at this point Lady Luck stepped in as she often does in sporting events. At race tracks ashore sometimes the leading horse stumbles or a jockey falls off. In boat races they occasionally break oars or catch crabs. In this case Iwo Jima's boat hit an almost submerged piece of driftwood with a sharp spike in it. This ripped an underwater gash in the cutter's thin bottom and water came squirting in by the bucketful. Soon it was sloshing around ankle-deep in the boat and she slowed down as if she were dragging her anchor. *Iwo Jima's* crew put up a gallant fight to coast in on their ten-length lead, but half a boat full of water is a much bigger handicap than a few barnacles on the bottom, synthetic or otherwise. The *Okinawa's* cutter crew, lifting their boat bodily with every stroke, overhauled their stricken rivals and surged across the finish line a full length in front.

Now it was the *Iwo Jima* rooters' turn to be stunned, to send up wails of anguish at their tough luck, and to hurl insults at the "lucky stiffs" who beat them. These insults were drowned out by delirious howls from the *Okinawa* crowd. They had won the race—and the money—so why dwell on that first mile-and-three-quarters nightmare?

On the judges' boat flags fluttered to the yardarm indicating "*Okinawa* wins, no protest."

Father O'Brien handed Fatso the "trophy" and said, "There you are Gioninni. It's all yours. But I think you people have used up all your luck for the rest of your lives. I wouldn't be surprised if the *Okinawa* capsizes tommorow. In fact, I may even say a prayer that she *does*."

"Thank you Padre, I guess we just live right on that bucket," said Fatso as he strapped the money belt under his shirt and waved for the *Okinawa's* motorboat to come alongside and take him and Beer Bottle ashore.

At the landing they instructed the motorboat to wait while they went up to the bank and converted the swag into lira for the payoff aboard ship. Coming back from the bank half an hour later they passed the Bucket Of Blood Bar and Grill and Beer Bottle said, "How about stopping in here for a scuttle of suds before we go back, Fatso?"

"Don't mind if I do," said Fatso sociably. "The first half of that race kind of shook me up—a splice in the main brace will do me good."

By the time Fatso and Beer Bottle sat down in the Bucket of Blood for a leisurely couple of beers, sinister events had taken place on the *Iwo Jima*. Their first boatload of rooters arrived back on board in a very agitated state. They had seen the *Okinawa's* motor whaleboat near the finish line with Web Foot in it just removing his frogman regalia, and some evil-minded sailor had ventured the theory that Web Foot had either planted the obstruction on which their boat foundered, or had swum under water and "torpedoed" the boat himself! By the time the mob of sore-headed losers in that boat got back to the ship, this outrageous figment of imagination, without a shred of truth in it, was accepted by all hands as gospel truth, and word of it spread through the ship like wildfire.

Angry voices resounded around the master-at-arms office, lifting the time honored cry, "We wuz robbed."

"We've just *had* it," muttered the CMAA bitterly. "The money has changed hands . . . we can't possibly get the Captain to take any official action . . . and there's nothing covering this sort of deal in the articles of the bet anyway . . . the lousy crooks—"

"Wait a minute," said Brizlinski. "That Gioninni guy went ashore to change the money into lira . . . they stole that money from us, so it don't belong to him and if we can catch him while he's still ashore . . ."

"Yeah," yelled a chorus of voices, "let's go ashore right now and get him—it's really our money anyway . . ."

It didn't take long to organize a large posse and get the Executive Officer to authorize a special boat to take them ashore. The Executive Officer agreed that official action was impossible and cautioned Brizlinski against precipitating any disturbance of the peace in a foreign port—but had the boat called away double time. Soon the posse piled out on the fleet landing and deployed into town in accordance with hastily prepared plans, leaving a strong detachment on the dock where the *Okinawa's* motorboat was waiting for Fatso.

In a few minutes Brizlinski and a trio of mean-looking huskies in the posse spotted Fatso and Beer Bottle seated in the Bucket Of Blood, and moved in on them.

"Hiya sailors," said Fatso in a genial mood. "Have a beer?"

"We wanna have a talk with you guys," said Brizlinski ominously.

Fatso noted that their attitude was hostile. "What's on your minds?" he asked sociably as he stepped on Beer Bottle's toe under the table meaning "stand by for heavy weather."

"That frogman," said Brizlinski. "What was he doing out there in that whaleboat?"

"What frogman?" demanded Fatso indignantly.

"Web Foot Foley—a couple of hundred of our people seen him in a boat close to the finish line, right after that hole got punched in our cutter."

"Oh-h-h—Web Foot," said Fatso. "Ha! Ha!—that don't mean nothing . . . he's nuts about swimming . . . he's always swimmin' around wherever we go—isn't he, Beer Bottle?"

"Stow that guff, Gioninni," said Brizlinski. "Your frogman punched that hole in our boat." The menacing scowls of Ski's posse confirmed this indictment.

Fatso was flabbergasted by this unjust accusation. It's the irony of fate that men who live by their wits often get away with murder

only to have a bum rap hung on them and go to jail for a misde-
meanor which they didn't commit.

"Why—he did NOT!" exclaimed Fatso piously. "He didn't do
no such a thing . . . he was just er . . . er . . ."

"Hand over that money belt," said Brizlinski in a menacing
manner. "Our crew had yours beat fair and square. We don't
wanna have no trouble, but we ain't going to stand for being
robbed."

The *Iwo Jima* mob were in an ugly mood, but Fatso and Beer
Bottle had been in tough jams together before. They knew instinctively what had to be done—and they did it! Fatso
suddenly threw his glass of beer in Brizlinski's face, whirled
around and dived out the window into an alley while Beer Bottle
capsized the table and waded into the four *Iwo Jima* sailors. While
Fatso fled down the alley, Beer Bottle fought a gallant delaying
action allowing Fatso to get about a half a block start before the
posse swarmed into the alley after him.

Fatso naturally headed for the dock and the sanctuary of the
Okinawa's motorboat. As he charged out onto the pier the *Iwo*'s
guard detail moved in around the boat ready to seize Fatso when
he tried to get in. By the time he saw them it was too late to turn
around—the pursuers from the café had him cut off behind. He
kept running full speed ahead, yelled at the dozing boat crew as
he passed them, plunged off the end of the dock and started
swimming. Two of the dock detail dove right in behind him but
ex-frogman Fatso soon left them behind.

But the help he expected from the motorboat failed him,
because the pursuers from the Bucket Of Blood promptly boarded
and captured the motorboat, the first such incident in the Mediterranean since the Barbary Pirates were exterminated. The
engineer, sizing up the situation accurately, dropped the ignition
key into the bilges, thus immobilizing the boat for pursuit.

Seeing the boat in hostile hands, Fatso swam for the dock on

143

the other side of the inlet—50 yards away by water but 600 yards by land around the inlet. He scrambled out of the water there about 200 yards ahead of the posse, who were running around the shore of the inlet, yelling "Stop thief" at the top of their lungs, and accumulating quite a following of citizens on their way around.

On the waterfront the world over, flight is considered a public confession of guilt. Any time waterfront people see one man running with several others raising a hue and cry pursuing him, they automatically join the pursuers and, if they catch the fugitive, they are apt to lynch him first and inquire into his offense after.

So, when Fatso took to his heels again, matters were rapidly becoming desperate. If that mob overhauled him, the *Iwo* boys would immediately snatch the money belt and then fling him to the wolves. His only hope was to stall off capture until the Navy Shore Patrol could arrive and take charge of the situation, but the chances of doing that seemed slim indeed, as the mob was gaining.

Fatso seized a forlorn hope. His flight took him past a stone watch tower of ancient vintage, which stuck up on the waterfront to a height of 150 feet, and was now used only by sightseers. The door stood open, the guard was asleep in his chair outside. Fatso veered toward it, plunged through the entrance and slammed the iron grille door behind him. A riot call had certainly gone in to police headquarters by this time and if he could lock that door long enough for the Shore Patrol to arrive, everything would be OK. At least his money belt would be safe—but there was no key!

Like a drowning man reaching for a straw, Fatso jumped into the elevator, pushed the button, and was on his way up to the top of the tower just as the vanguard of the mob reached the door. At the top Fatso jammed the elevator door open, stalling the elevator in the up position and cutting off that means of pursuit. A timid-looking Italian maiden cringed against the railing of the observation platform and regarded Fatso suspiciously.

Quickly casing the joint, Fatso found one doorway opening on to a spiral stairway that wound downward round and round the walls of the tower—a relic of the earlier century in which the tower was built. Heavy bolts on the inside of this doorway enabled the guard to lock it from the top platform before making his last daily trip down in the modern elevator. Footsteps of the mob were already pounding up this stairway when Fatso slid the bolts into place and sat down on the floor to rest, the Italian girl moving nervously to the opposite side of the platform. Just as Fatso was regaining his breath the vanguard of the posse arrived at the top of the stairs, all out of breath, and began hammering on the door.

"Open up!" they demanded.

"Nuts!" came the reply from within—given just as defiantly as General McAuliffe once gave it.

"Open up in the name of the law," growled a voice. "This is Lieutenant Blatz of the Shore Patrol."

Maybe it was the Shore Patrol officer and maybe it wasn't. There was no way Fatso could tell—and so no reply from within.

There was only room for two abreast on the stairs so there was a traffic jam at the dead end.

"Bust the door down," yelled a voice in the rear.

The two men at the head of the line put their shoulders against it and heaved—with no result. They eased back and threw their weight against it, but it was a stout oak door and the bolts were strong. It held like a solid bulkhead.

"Let's all hit it at once," yelled someone from behind. "Stand by-y-y, one, two, three, HEAVE!"

The door trembled as the weight of a dozen bodies crashed against it and a howl of pain went up from the two human battering rams at the head of the line who got a couple of cracked ribs out of the effort.

"Again," yelled the voice in the rear. "Stand BY-Y-Y-Y . . ."

Now, Hear This!

"Belay that! Lay off! Nothin' doing!" yelled the two battering rams in unison. "Send down and get a couple of fire axes."

This word was passed back down the line and Fatso realized he was just stalling off the inevitable—there was no escape. But there was likewise no such word in Fatso's book as surrender. After all, he belonged to the same Navy as John Paul Jones and Lawrence. I doubt if he could tell you which one said, "Don't give up the ship," and which, "I have not yet begun to fight." But Fatso thoroughly subscribed to both sentiments at the present moment.

He strode over to the railing around the observation platform and peered over the side. There was a sheer drop of 150 feet and a hostile, howling mob at the bottom—no hope there!

Fatso was not a conspicuously religious man. I doubt very much that he prayed at this moment. In fact, he would probably tell you that any healthy man should be ashamed to ask for outside help in a fight. But be that as it may, a passing thought of St. Anne's Orphanage and the pious sisters flashed through his mind. It occurred to him that $75 was an odd figure and perhaps $100 would be better. Whether this amounts to a prayer or not I can't say, but at least coming from a rough-and-ready character like Fatso, it apparently did. Because at that very moment an angel appeared in the sky—the *Okinawa*'s whirly bird angel, fluttering in from the ship to pick up the mail. It was heading to pass the tower close aboard at an altitude of 200 feet.

Fatso was no expert on miracles and to this day he can't tell you whether this really was one or not. But no matter what it was, if he could attract the attention of that whirly bird, he might get out of this jam not only with his hide intact, but also his money belt. All he needed now was a distress signal.

He quickly unbuttoned his trousers, slipped out of them and seized a broom that was leaning against the cupola. At this point the Sicilian maiden let out a scream, sank to her knees, buried her face in her hands and started to pray. I can understand her alarm when Fatso took off his pants, but I haven't any idea what she thought he was going to do with the broom! Using the fly of his pants for the hoist of the flag, Fatso improvised a new signal flag on the spot, scrambled up on top of the cupola, and waved the banner frantically as the whirly bird approached.

In the whirly bird Web Foot Foley was seated alongside the pilot, admiring the famous Palermo scenery and discussing the boat race.

"Yessir, we wuz certainly lucky today," he said. "They would of beat us by a nautical mile if it hadn't been for that accident— and take it from me sir, that *Iwo Jima* crew is good—they can row much faster than they did today—I *know* what I'm talking about too," he added mysteriously—"Say! Look at that guy waving at us on the watch tower, sir."

"Friendly people, these Eyetalians," observed the pilot. "They always wave at you."

"Yabbut they don't take off their pants and wave 'em, at least not the men," said Web Foot. "I think there's something funny happening over there."

The pilot saw merit in this last observation and brought the helicopter to a hovering position with the watch tower a hundred yards abeam while he and Web Foot peered at the strange apparition on top of the cupola. As soon as they began hovering, Fatso dropped the flag and began making semaphore signals with his arms.

All frogmen are experts at semaphore, so Web Foot called the signals aloud—"SOS . . . SOS . . . he's sending SOS, sir!"

"We better go over closer and see what it's all about."

As the whirly bird sidled over, Web Foot suddenly let out a whoop. "That's Fatso Gioninni sir—that's who it is! And he's in bad trouble too—look at that mob around the bottom of the tower, and all those fire engines, ambulances, and police cars— it must be a riot—we better get him offa there sir. Shall I rig out the sling, sir?"

"Yeah—go ahead," said the pilot, easing the angel over to a point about 20 feet directly above Fatso as the horse collar swung out and lowered away.

Fatso was snatched from the hot seat just seconds before the fire axes hacked through the door and the angry mob swarmed onto the observation platform. The Sicilian maiden, with her face buried in her hands, never saw the helicopter, and to this day she considers Fatso's sudden disappearance a true miracle.

A few minutes later the whirly bird deposited Fatso—minus his pants but plus his money belt—on the flight deck of the *Okinawa* and fluttered off again on the interrupted mail trip.

To most sailors it would be quite embarrassing indeed to be set down in the middle of the flight deck in broad daylight wearing a dress jumper but no hat or pants. Hilarious comments were hurled from the signal bridge suggesting ribald reasons for this strange manner of returning from liberty—some of them reflecting on Fatso's moral character. But he strode across the deck with dignity and aplomb and disappeared below toward the incinerator.

That night a heated debate took place in the inner sanctum.

"I tell ya we ought to keel-haul that guy and run him clean offa this ship," declared Satchelaft, coxswain of the racing cutter. This statement was the peroration of a long harangue, and "that guy" was of course Web Foot Foley. Satchelaft had related how he dove under the boat right after the race and found six suction cups fastened on *his* boat instead of *Iwo Jima*'s. He hurled angry charges that Web Foot was a dirty double-crosser and had probably bet on the *Iwo Jima*.

"Now wait a minute," said Fatso. "This frogman racket isn't as easy as most of you pond lilies think. Mistakes can happen and that's all this was—if Foley had been betting on *Iwo Jima* he would have left me there on top of that tower to be lynched so he could collect his dough. But I paid him 150 bucks he had coming out of our pot just before he went on liberty this afternoon."

All hands except Satchelaft nodded agreement with Fatso's analysis.

"So now," said Fatso, "all we gotta do to wind up this deal is send somebody ashore to pay for that window I busted in the Bucket Of Blood. Let the *Iwo Jima* worry about pacifying the local cops for the damage to their tower."

Next day Fatso sent Father O'Brien $25.00 more for St. Anne's from the breakage pot, and has been remembered in the prayers of the sisters ever since.

⚓ CHAPTER EIGHT

Water Shortage

IN THE CAPTAIN's cabin of the *Okinawa*, several senior officers had met to discuss the alarming expenditure rate of fresh water on the ship. The whole Eastern Mediterranean area was currently suffering from a severe drought and the situation was becoming critical on certain islands such as Crete. But this had nothing to do with the *Okinawa*'s troubles. Naval ships make their own fresh water. The Chief Engineer was summing up after telling a long sad story:

"Captain, these post-war sailors just don't understand the value of fresh water and this crew of ours is wasting water a lot faster than I can make it. The supply in the ship's tanks has been going down steadily for the past two weeks even though I've had the evaporators going full blast all the time. We've just got to start rationing fresh water, and that's all there is to it."

"I guess you're right, Chief," said the Captain reluctantly, "I hate to do this. But we've tried everything else and it hasn't done any good. OK—put water hours into effect tomorrow."

All around the table heads nodded grave agreement with this unpleasant command decision, and the meeting adjourned.

Next morning long lines of sailors formed outside each one of the crew's wash rooms. Fresh water, instead of being available twenty-four hours a day, was now turned on in the wash bowls and showers for only one hour in the morning and evening. This was a grievous hardship to all on board because it meant you had to stand in line for half an hour just to wash your face and hands. You could have all the salt water you wanted without waiting, but washing in salt water leaves you feeling as if you had scrubbed down in glue. It's like trying to make love wearing a winter flying suit and heavy leather mittens. It's unsatisfactory.

"Where do they get this stuff, rationing water," growled a Marine near the end of the line. "We got a right to have water. Don't we?"

"Well, you see," said the sailor behind him, "this here Mediterranean Sea is salt water and we gotta distill the sea water to get the salt out of it. The Black Gang claims that we been using 150,000 gallons a day, and they can't distill it that fast."

"I don't believe it," said the Marine. "That's 50 gallons per man, a whole gasoline drum full of water. You know darned well nobody uses that much."

"Yabbut that includes everything," said the sailor. "Water for the boilers, the galley, the laundry, the scuttlebutts, the washrooms, and the officers' country too. I'll bet them officers use half of it. Some of these new ensigns we got on board probably think the ocean is fresh water."

"I don't know about that," muttered the Leatherneck. "But I think it stinks in more ways than one when they won't give you enough water to take a bath on a ship as big as this."

"I suppose in Korea the top sergeant drew a warm bath in a tub for you every morning?"

"Korea was different, but I'm going to beat this game," said the Marine craftily. "I got a bucket, and I'm going to fill it up every time they turn the water on and keep it in my locker so I'll have it when I want it."

"They thought of that too, soldier," observed his friend.

Now, Hear This!

"There's an eagle-eyed master-at-arms at the head of this line and you can either use a wash bowl or shower, or else take about a cupful of water out in a bucket, but not both. There's nothin' you can do about it but ship over in the Army next time."

While this conversation was going on down on the berth deck, Fatso was tinkering around in his incinerator compartment on the starboard side of the hangar deck.

At this moment he was in a corner behind the big furnace, screwing a length of one-inch pipe with a spigot on the end of it into a larger pipe running through the compartment. The larger pipe supplied fresh water to the Captain's and Admiral's cabins on the *Okinawa,* and naturally water rationing was not going to affect the supply of fresh water in *that* pipe. Neither was it going to affect Fatso's supply, after he got this plumbing job completed.

You might say that in some way Fatso drew almost as much water on the *Okinawa* as the Skipper. When he got this spigot installed this would be true literally as well as figuratively.

It is fundamental in the Navy that long years of faithful service earn certain privileges. As Fatso saw it, this water rationing order certainly had nothing to do with old seafaring men like the Admiral, the Captain—or himself.

That night just before taps Fatso's cronies began drifting into the inner sanctum in accordance with their regular custom. Half a dozen of them were seated around the inner sanctum when the door opened and admitted Scuttlebutt, covered with grease and sweat.

"This is a hell of a way to run a Navy," remarked Scuttlebutt to the assembled crowd. "Here I come off a 4-hour watch below and the water is shut off all over the ship. I'm the 'Fresh Water King' of this bucket and *I* can't even get a bath. What I want to know, Fatso, is how long can you go without a bath?"

"That all depends on how dirty you don't mind being," answered Fatso philosophically. "But, since you're a friend of mine,

152

just get yourself a bucket, hang it under the spigot behind the furnace and you can have all the fresh water you want."

Fatso's revelation of this new convenience of the "club" was greeted enthusiastically by all hands. Each new arrival that evening was proudly informed of it and added his approval.

About a half hour after taps Fatso remarked, "I wonder what's holding up old Bellyache—I'm getting hungry." Bellyache was the head man in the crew's galley. It was his duty each evening to bring up a basket full of steaks, eggs, bread, butter, and various trimmings to be cooked and eaten in the incinerator compartment. This was a custom of long standing in Fatso's inner sanctum, just as much a matter of routine on the *Okinawa* as hoisting the colors each morning at eight bells.

"I think I hear him coming now," said Beer Bottle.

It was indeed Bellyache that Beer Bottle heard coming, but he entered with a long face and with no basket. There was a shocked silence for a moment and then Fatso said, "What-ho, Bellyache, where's the grub? We're all gettin' hungry."

"There ain't gonna be no more grub," said Bellyache as if he were announcing that the end of the world would occur at 7 bells of the current watch.

This statement was greeted with outraged and unbelieving protests from all hands almost as incredulous as if he had made such a prediction. It took Bellyache some time to quiet them down so he could explain.

"It's this new Paymaster we got the other day. He's always popping into the galley at odd times and he won't stand for no monkey business. I mean for sure. He put a mess cook on the report today for swiping a couple of apples out of a whole barrel full."

"But there was no monkey business about what we were doing," said Fatso indignantly. "We weren't *swiping* that stuff."

"That's right, certainly not. Of course we weren't swiping it,"

153

agreed Bellyache emphatically, "It was . . . it was . . . just stuff that happened to be left over when I got through feeding the crew. You can't make things come out exactly even when you cook for 3,000 men. Can you?"

"Of course not," agreed Fatso. "And this left-over stuff would of been thrun out and wasted if you hadn't brought it up here. Wouldn't it?" he demanded righteously.

"Well—not *exactly*, maybe," said Bellyache thinking of the dozen sirloin steaks that always happened to be left over even when the crew had beans for dinner.

"What are we gonna do about this?" asked Fatso addressing the gathering. "We certainly gotta eat!"

"Couldn't we get the, er—left-overs, out of the butcher shop before they go up to the galley, so the Paymaster wouldn't know about it?" asked Satchelaft. "Then there wouldn't be no left-overs in the galley for the Paymaster to squawk about. Things would come out exactly even—no waste at all."

"You can't get nothing from nowhere without this long-nosed guy knowing it," said Bellyache sadly. "He's snooping around checking up all the time. He weighs everything down to the ounce, and I'll bet he'd find out if even a cracker got adrift."

In the next fifteen minutes many schemes for obtaining food were proposed, examined, and rejected. The situation looked grim. All this time "Judge" Jenks, the Executive Officer's yeoman was in deep thought, taking no part in the discussion. Judge was one of the legal experts of the crowd, being the courts-martial yeoman for the ship and a recognized authority of the U.S. Navy Regulations.

"There is one way we could do this," remarked the Judge, clearing his throat—"We could buy the stuff."

Indignant snorts greeted this announcement. It was almost unthinkable to *buy* the stuff. The only thing worse than that would be to go without. Finally Fatso demanded scornfully,

"What do you mean, buy the stuff?"

"I mean buy it like the other messes on the ship do," replied the Judge. "The Admiral, the Captain, the Wardroom and the Chiefs, they all buy their food from the Paymaster's stores and it's perfectly legal and regulation."

"Yabbut this guy won't sell it to no unauthorized mess like this one," said Bellyache. "You gotta think of something better than that."

"We can wangle it through the Captain's mess," said the Judge. "Fatso,—wasn't the Captain's steward one of the guys you saved when the *Franklin* got hit and they had that big fire down on the hangar deck?"

"Yeah, that's right," said Fatso. "Old Garcia Mendez. I got scorched kinda bad myself dragging him out of the cabin pantry."

"Well," said the Judge, "Suppose we have Garcia draw whatever stuff we need with the Captain's stores. We get it from him and pay him cash for it. At the end of the month, when he settles the Captain's bill, he just adds our money to what the Captain gives him. The government gets paid for every bit of the stuff we use, the Captain only pays for his own stuff, and nobody gets gypped or ever knows the difference. It don't cost the taxpayers nothing. We *give away* millions for foreign aid and for farmers. This thing would be a sound economic program."

The idea was examined from all angles and nobody could find any flaws in it.

"The next question is," said the Judge, "where do we get the money from? I guess we'll have to start charging dues for Fatso's old sailors' home here. How much a day will it cost us, Bellyache, to live in the style to which we are entitled?"

Bellyache did some figuring and said, "I would think about a dollar and a half per man per day."

"Hmm," said Beer Bottle, "Forty-five bucks a month! We don't all of us have that kind of money." All the heads nodded sad agreement.

After a long pause, Fatso said thoughtfully, "Maybe I've got an idea about how to do it. That food has already been bought for us once by the government. I don't see why we should dig down in our own jeans for money to buy it again and maybe we don't have to."

Although nobody knew what Fatso had in mind, all indicated emphatic agreement with whatever it was.

"How much do you think," asked Fatso, "a bucket of fresh water is worth nowadays on this ship?"

"Depends on how bad you need a bath and how the guys who've gotta live with you feel about it," said Beer Bottle. "Maybe two bits, if you smell bad enough. What's that got to do with it?"

"Well," said Fatso, "I've got a water supply here all day long now. We'll need about twenty dollars a day to pay for our chow. If I could sell eighty buckets of water a day at two bits a throw . . ."

All hands indicated jubilant agreement with this stroke of genius.

Finally Satchelaft said, "I dunno. It sounds kind of illegal to me. Wouldn't that be selling government property?"

The Judge considered the legal aspects of this question and handed down an opinion. "Naw. To make a conviction stick under that charge the property has to be of some value. The government gives this water away for nothing, doesn't it? So, we're not doing anything illegal by selling it to guys silly enough to pay for it."

"As a matter of fact," said Fatso, "we'll be doing the taxpayers a big favor selling it. That's the best way in the world to teach this crew of drugstore cowboys the value of fresh water. The officers can preach to them about it till they're blue in the face and it won't do no good. But let 'em pay hard cash for it and they'll soon learn."

All hands concurred with this theory, so they got busy and mapped out a program for handling the sale and distribution of water.

The next day was a busy one for Fatso. It doesn't take long for the "word" to spread all over the ship when some new and slightly shady enterprise is afloat. Each of Fatso's cronies dropped a word here and there during the morning watch, and by noon everyone who wanted fresh water bad enough knew where they could get it.

Soon Fatso was doing a land-office business. It involved practically no risk of being caught, because water rationing was about as popular with the crew as prohibition had been with the country some years before. No sailor would report this thing to the officers any more than a citizen would turn in his bootlegger during the prohibition era. Fatso's regular occupation was a perfect front for the new racket. Traffic around the incinerator increased considerably but this didn't arouse the curiosity of any officer because sailors are carrying buckets of trash up to the incinerator all day long. They are always lugging buckets of salt water around the ship too, and you can't tell from looking at a bucket of water whether it is fresh or salt.

That night the club met in a jubilant mood. There had been no difficulty arranging the deal with Garcia, the Captain's steward. Garcia was a simple straightforward soul who felt that he was under obligation to anyone who had saved his life. He delivered a basketful of steaks, eggs, and bread to the incinerator just after taps and threw in some olives, celery, potatoes, and onions, that weren't on Fatso's grocery order, but which were left over from the Captain's table.

While the steaks were sizzling, Fatso reported on the day's operations to the board of directors. "Two hundred buckets of water at two bits a bucket—that makes fifty smackers. This stuff we're eating tonight only cost us eighteen bucks, so we make a clear profit of thirty-two dollars. This thing is like a gold mine, or striking oil."

"You know," said Beer Bottle stuffing a big hunk of steak in his mouth, "this water rationing is going to be the best thing ever happened to this ship."

"That's right," agreed the Judge. "Make that steak of mine medium rare, Bellyache."

"Matter of fact," said Fatso between mouthfuls, "it will improve the battle efficiency of the ship too. When these kids learn the value of fresh water, we'll burn a lot less fuel oil and we'll save the taxpayers thousands of dollars."

"Not if you keep on selling it hand over fish," observed Satchel-aft. "Water consumption will go *up*—instead of down."

"Aw, eighty buckets is nothing," said Fatso. "Why, even if I sold five hundred buckets that's only 1,500 gallons. We've been using 150,000 gallons a day up till now, so that would only be 1 per cent of the total. It ain't even hardly—well—a drop in the bucket."

"The water consumption has dropped way down already," said Scuttlebutt whose job it was as "Fresh Water King" to sound the tanks every day, keep track of the figures, and run the pumps. "These guys are learning fast."

"It's like anything else," said Fatso. "You don't know how good a thing is till they take it away from you and in this modern Navy with washbowls all over the ship, they take too much for granted. Now, you take me for instance, I *lived* out of a bucket my first two cruises in this Navy. I'll bet even some of you guys never had to do that."

Several paused in their steak eating long enough to admit this accusation.

"Why," said Fatso, "they used to give us a half a bucket of water a day and that's all you got. You'd brush your teeth first, then shave, then take a salt-water shower and rinse off with fresh water in your bucket, saving every drop of the fresh water so you could scrub your skivvies in it later."

A bunch of well-fed sailors at peace with the world fall into a reminiscent mood very easily. "I can remember," said the Judge, "on the old *Tuscarora*, when Billygoat Jones was skipper back in 1935. We was surveying the equator and boy, it was hot. But half of a bucket every *other* day was all *we* got. So we used to keep the awnings spread and we had rain barrels all over the ship wherever the awnings drained. That way we got all the water we needed—it rains a lot down there on the equator and I remember . . . ."

When the clambake broke up that evening, the general feeling was that everything was squared away and all was well. For a few days things continued that way, getting even better, in fact. By the fourth day water sales were up to 380 buckets. That night Fatso's treasury showed a surplus of $135.00 for the four days' operations, even after deducting for the chow.

"Boy, ain't this something," said Fatso. "Instead of retiring at the end of this cruise I think I'll ship over again, if I can get on this ship."

But at this point a small cloud appeared on the horizon. "You talk as if this was going to last forever," observed Scuttlebutt, the "Fresh Water King." "But we've been saving so much water we're almost caught up now, and water hours will probably be abolished in another couple of days."

This was a rude jolt to all hands, one that nobody had foreseen. The world over, whenever people start getting something for nothing they think it's going to last forever. Nobody expects their oil well to run dry.

"Wait a minute now," said Fatso, "that's going to be bad. This Paymaster will still keep charging us for our grub. If you stop rationing water it will cut our food off. We can't let that happen."

"Well, it's going to happen, and pretty soon," predicted

Now, Hear This!

Scuttlebutt. "Water consumption is way the hell-and-gone down. This rationing has made everybody water-conscious and the galley and laundry are only using about half as much as they used to. That's where the big saving comes in, not from the washrooms."

"Why don't you cut down on the evaporators and just not make so much," asked Satchelaft. "That would keep up the shortage."

"I don't have nothing to say about the evaps," said Scuttlebutt. "The assistant Engineer Officer tells them what to do and he's got 'em going full blast twenty-four hours a day and checks up on them like a hawk. I just take the water that they make, pump it around into the various storage tanks, and keep the records on it."

"Can't you fudge a little bit on the records," asked Satchelaft. "You could keep on reporting high consumption every day and nobody would know the difference."

"Yeah. That's what I *been* doing. But my tanks have got 100,000 more gallons in them than I'm reporting right now. They're getting filled up. I won't have room for no more water pretty soon."

The board of strategy immediately went to work on this new problem. All sorts of bookkeeping dodges were proposed, but Scuttlebutt kept insisting that the bookkeeping was the least of his worries. There were dozens of ways to make the figures look right on paper, but his problem was where the hell to put all that water that the evaps were making.

Finally Fatso hit on a solution. "Look," he said, "this ship has got hundreds of double-bottom compartments with nothing in them. They've all got connections for flooding and pumping them to take care of battle damage. Why don't you just put the excess water in one of them for a while? 100,000 gallons is only about 300 tons. Compared to the tonnage of this ship, that's just a fart in a whirlwind."

This was regarded by all hands, except Scuttlebutt, as another stroke of genius on Fatso's part. In this way it seemed that water rationing could be prolonged almost indefinitely. Scuttlebutt knew he would be hung at the yardarm if he were caught at this business, but the others finally talked him into it, although he instinctively knew there was a "bug" in it.

So, the evaporators boiled merrily away, making water galore; rationing continued making the crew more and more water-conscious; and actual daily consumption dropped to only 50,000 gallons, about one-third what it used to be. But Scuttlebutt kept reporting the consumption figure at about 100,000 gallons, so that meant he had 50,000 gallons a day that he had to hide in the double bottoms. Meantime, the money rolled in up in Fatso's sanctum and by the end of two more weeks the surplus was $1,003.50. Disposal of the excess profits was also becoming a problem, so the club began to lay plans for a whale of a binge ashore in Lisbon with the accumulated surplus.

"This is better," remarked Fatso, "than running a gin mill on the dock in Panama during fleet maneuvers."

But all good things must come to an end and finally the balloon blew up. One night the Judge came hurrying into the inner sanctum and announced to the steak-eaters, "Boys, we got trouble."

"How come," demanded Scuttlebutt between mouthfuls.

"You ought to know," said the Judge, "because you're the guy who's got the most of it. How much extra water have you got hid in the double bottoms now?"

"Oh, I dunno," said Scuttlebutt. "I guess about 400,000 gallons, but there's plenty more room down there. This is the biggest ship in the Navy."

"Yeah," said the Judge, "but you can sink any ship in the whole world if you put enough water in it. 400,000 gallons of water is pretty near 1,200 tons. Did you ever think of that?"

"No," said Scuttlebutt, "but shucks, this ship displaces pretty near 60,000 . . ."

"Yeah, but look. I was just talking to a quartermaster who takes the draft figures every day. While you been stowing water in the bottoms, we've been burning oil, and so the draft of the ship has been coming up slowly like it should between fuelings. But pretty soon we will fill up with oil again and then we'll be caught with our pants down. It will show up in the draft figures right away. 1,200 tons of water will make this ship draw 8 inches more than she should. What are you gonna do about that?"

This was a shocking development to all hands, especially to Scuttlebutt, who would be holding the sack, or perhaps more accurately, the bucket.

"Well—can't we get the quartermaster to fudge a little on the draft figures?" asked Scuttlebutt.

"Not a chance," said the Judge. "In the first place, everybody would notice right away that the gangway platforms were closer to the water than they should be after the next refueling, and you couldn't miss seeing it on the waterline of the ship. Besides that, we draw so much water anyway that we gotta come in to some of these Mediterranean harbors on high tide to get over the bar. Eight inches extra draft could run us aground. You just gotta get rid of that water before we refuel again."

"Couldn't you just pump it overboard?" asked the Marine Top Sergeant.

Scuttlebutt looked at the Leatherneck as if he had just spit tobacco juice on the quarterdeck. A sailor man of Scuttlebutt's type would no more think of pumping fresh water overboard than he would of treason. He'd go to jail first. "What kind of a left-handed rubber swab handle do you think I am?" demanded Scuttlebutt.

Scuttlebutt was thinking fast and hoping for some suggestion, but none was forthcoming. Finally, he said desperately, "I'll just tell the Chief Engineer my tanks are all full. Then he'll shut down his evaps and I'll use it up out of the bottoms."

"Boy, what a sharp operator you are," said the Judge. "I don't suppose the Chief will give it a second thought when you keep on reporting 100,000 gallons used every day and the tanks stay full with the evaps shut down. This Chief Engineer ain't very smart, but I doubt if he's that dumb."

"I guess you're right," said Scuttlebutt miserably. "If I can't figure out something before we refuel, I guess I'll just have to take the rap." And, on that depressing note the meeting adjourned.

At this same moment another grave conference was in progress in the Captain's cabin between the Old Man, the Exec and the Chief Engineer. They were studying the following dispatch from the CinC to the *Okinawa*.

ISLAND OF CRETE IS SUFFERING FROM PROLONGED DROUGHT. TOWN OF IRAKLION MUST HAVE 300,000 GAL- LONS FRESH WATER IMMEDIATELY. GREEK GOVERNMENT URGENTLY REQUESTS ASSISTANCE. CAN YOU SUPPLY WATER.

This put the *Okinawa* over a barrel. If she gave that much water away she would be left high and dry herself because of her own extravagance and wasteful methods. But the one thing no Navy Captain wants to do is to reply to an inquiry from the Commander in Chief saying, "No can do."

"Well, how about it, Chief?" asked the Skipper dubiously.

"It's impossible, Captain," said the Chief glumly. "We're just barely holding our own now with the evaps going full blast and making 100,000 gallons a day. I hate to let you down this way, Cap'n, but we're just up against cold facts. Even if our tanks were full, we couldn't give them 300,000 gallons."

"It's going to make us look awful bad," said the Captain, "if I have to answer that message and explain we can't do it because we waste so much water ourselves."

The Exec and Chief ruefully agreed that this was indeed true. But could offer no suggestions.

"Let me sleep on this," said the Captain, wishing to postpone the inevitable as long as possible. On that pessimistic note the conference adjourned.

When word of this dispatch and the proposed answer got down to Fatso's inner sanctum—as word of every important decision on the *Okinawa* always did very quickly—Fatso's face lit up.

"Well, I'll be dipped in gook," he said, "I guess we just live right."

A few minutes later the Marine orderly informed the Captain rather dubiously that one Gioninni, bosun's mate first class, requested an audience with him. If any other sailor on the ship had made such a request late in the evening, the Captain would probably have told the Marine to take him down to sick bay and have his head examined. But Fatso was a special case. Paddling around after the Lexington got sunk and holding the Skipper's head out of water had established a camaraderie between them not usually found between four-stripe Captains and bosuns' mates first class.

"Send him in," said the Captain to the surprised Marine.

"Hello, Fatso," said the Captain sociably. "And what kind of a jam are you in now?"

"I ain't in no jam, Cap'n," said Fatso, "I just wanted to make a suggestion sir, that I think would be of benefit to the ship."

"Oh?" said the Captain, on his guard immediately. "You're sure it's the *ship* that will benefit from this?"

"Yes *Sir*," said Fatso. "But, Cap'n, if you don't mind my saying so, it would have to be handled very carefully."

This statement confirmed the Captain's suspicions, and doubly on guard he said, "And just what is this proposition of yours, Gioninni?"

"Well Sir, Cap'n," said Fatso, "I would like to respectively suggest that we give them Greeks that there water they want."

The Captain shot a shrewd look at Fatso to see if he was drunk. Satisfied on that score he said, "Well now, Gioninni, that's very nice indeed of you to come all the way up here to tell me that—"

"Yessir, I know Sir," Fatso interrupted, "it's none of my business, Cap'n and maybe some people think we can't afford it, but we *can* do it, Sir."

"That's ridiculous, you know what the water situation is on the ship. HOW could we do it?"

"That there is the one question I'm hoping you won't make me answer Sir," said Fatso. "But I *know* we CAN do it."

Knowing Fatso as he did, the Skipper knew that such a statement from Fatso, no matter how wildly improbable it sounded, was credible. His eyes narrowed and, after a minute's thought, they began to bulge and he said, "Well I'll be . . . do you mean to stand there and tell me that you've got pretty near half a million gallons of water stashed away somewhere on this ship?"

"Nossir, Cap'n," said Fatso piously. "That ain't what I *said*, Sir—but now that you've brung the subject up, there is a certain amount of truth in it. You can give them Greeks 300,000 gallons and never miss it, Sir."

The Captain eyed Fatso with mingled emotions of righteous wrath and grudging admiration. "Where the hell is it?" he demanded, "In the double bottoms?"

Fatso smirked coyly and said, "Yessir. You shore guessed it, Cap'n."

"I ought to keelhaul you and fling you in the brig for the rest of this cruise," said the Captain, trying his best to assume a baleful scowl.

"Yessir," said Fatso. "But them Greeks will be very grateful to the Admiral for that there water, Cap'n."

"Get the hell out of here, you blackmailer," snorted the Captain.

Now, Hear This!

"I should have gone down with the *Lexington* instead of letting you save me."

"Aye aye, Sir," said Fatso, cracking up with a snappy salute, executing about face, and retiring from the cabin.

As Fatso disappeared with a satisfied grin on his face, the Captain reached for a dispatch blank and wrote his answer to the Commander in Chief's message, "Can Do."

Both the Commander and Chief Engineer protested against sending this message and thought the Captain must have gone off his rocker.

"Why Cap'n," said the Commander, "it will take all the water we've got on board plus all we can make in two days."

"Yes I know," said the Captain with a look of bold determination on his face. "But I have a great confidence in you and Chief Engineer. I'm sure you both know *all* the angles of this water business, and I'm sure you won't let me down on this."

"But CAPTAIN," they both said in alarm.

"But me no buts," said the Captain. "My mind is made up."

The two officers left the cabin muttering to themselves, and as soon as they got outside, the Commander shook his head sadly and made circular motions with his finger around his temple.

Next day, the *Okinawa* anchored in Suda Bay, Crete, and pumped nearly half a million gallons of fresh water into barges. After a couple of hours' pumping the Chief, who as Fatso said, was a little slow in the uptakes, began to smell a rat and when he found his regular water tanks were still full, he popped down below and checked the valves of Scuttlebutt's headquarters. That let the cat out of the bag—or at least left the Chief now holding the mouth of the bag, so he could let the cat out *if* he wanted to.

A short time later he appeared in the Exec's cabin and said rather sheepishly, "Commander, we've been taken for a sleigh ride—" and explained the whole deal.

"Looks to me like that 'Fresh Water King' of yours and maybe

166

some other people in your department are due for courts-martial," observed the Commander.

"They certainly are," said the Chief, "but there's one angle to this we've got to consider. The Captain must have found out about this before we did, otherwise he never would have agreed to give all that water away."

"By golly, you're right," said the Commander. "Makes *us* look kind of foolish, as if we didn't know what goes on on this ship, doesn't it? Remember how he said 'I'm sure you both know ALL the angles' last night? I guess the thing for us to do is just wait for the Old Man to say something. Maybe he won't be too anxious to air this deal either—after all, we're making a lot of character with the CinC by being able to supply the Greeks. He probably wouldn't want the Admiral to find out how we actually did it."

That evening there was a meeting in the Captain's cabin to discuss the water situation. The Chief Engineer opened the discussion. "Cap'n, due to rather—uh—er—unexpected improvement in the water consumption, I think we can now dispense with water rationing."

The Damage Control Officer cut in with, "It's just like I said three weeks ago, Captain. All we needed was getting tough for a while. Now that educational program I put on—"

"It was very good," interrupted the Exec. "And I have no doubt it had something to do with the improvement."

"I saved a lot of water in the galley too," said the Paymaster smugly.

"And I started a new system in the laundry saving thousands of gallons," said the First Lieutenant, climbing on the bandwagon.

"How about your department, Chief?" asked the Captain, eyeing the Chief Engineer narrowly. "No doubt the Black Gang had a lot to do with this phenomenal improvement too . . . didn't you stop a lot of leaks—tighten up on loose gaskets—and maybe find more economical ways of running the engines?"

Now, Hear This!

"Well sir," said the Chief warily, "I would prefer to let results speak for themselves. I'm sure you know at least as much as the rest of us about what . . . er . . . actually transpired . . . so I don't think it's necessary to hash over the details."

"You're absolutely right, Chief," said the Captain. "There's no use borrowing trouble by trying to decide who had most to do with this improvement. The main thing is to continue our efforts and hold the gains we have made. However, we can cancel water-rationing tomorrow for the time being. Thank you, gentlemen and good night."

Down in the incinerator, Fatso Gioninni was saying, "Pass the salt, butter, and onions, please."

"Just give me three eggs with my steak, Bellyache," said Beer Bottle Bates. "I ain't very hungry tonight."

⚓ CHAPTER NINE

Fatso's Bomb-Disposal Job

As THE OKINAWA approached her anchorage in Naples, Dopey Dugan leaned over the side from the leadsman's platform on the foc'sle swinging his lead like a pendulum in gradually increasing arcs. When he got up enough momentum he wound it around in a complete circle up over his head and down behind him. As it started the ascending arc forward again he let the lead fly, paying out the carefully coiled line from his left hand. As the lead plunked to the bottom he hauled in the slack briskly with both hands while his striker faked it down on the deck, keeping the line taut as the ship ran ahead. As he passed over the lead with the line vertical, Dopey cocked a careful eye at the red marker rag just at the water's edge and sang out, "By the ma-a-ark seven, Sir," thus informing the bridge they were in seven fathoms of water.

Of course, the bridge knew this already from the automatic fathometer, which is faster and more dependable than the hand lead. But there is a Navy regulation of ancient vintage dating back to the days of sail still on the books, which says the leadsman shall be in the chains when entering port. So every new ship we build in the atomic age still has leadsman's platforms, and prudent Captains keep them manned when on soundings.

By the time Dopey got his line made up again ready for another cast, the ship was nearing the anchorage. Winding up for his next heave, Dopey felt the foc'sle tremble from the engines backing, and as he made the cast the Chief Bosun up forward bellowed, "Let go the port anchor."

A husky sailor clouted the pelican hook with a 20-pound sledge and leaped clear as the huge anchor chain crashed across the deck and down the hawsepipe. Dopey's 5-pound lead and the great 30-ton bower anchor plunged to the bottom together. Now Dopey's job was to tell the bridge what the ship was doing. "Forging ahead rapidly," he sang out as the ship overran his lead—and the anchor.

The Bosun goggled over the side at the headway and waved at the men on the wildcat brakes to let the chain run, as the 35-fathom shackle plunged down the hawsepipe. The ship quaked violently as the bridge rang up "full speed astern" and the engine rooms spun their throttles wide open.

You've only got 140 fathoms in an anchor cable, and if you tear the bitter end out of the chain locker you can wreck the foc'sle and kill some men. "Check her handsomely," yelled the bosun to the wildcat operators as the 80-fathom shackle shot by him.

After another quick look over the side he bawled, "All hands clear the foc'sle! Get aft of them wildcats." Dopey dropped lead, line, and all over the side as he scrambled on deck and ran aft with the rest of the fleeing sailors.

As the 110-fathom shot clattered out of the dog house, the bosun, still up forward in contempt of his own orders, yelled, "HOLD FAST—" and the wildcat men spun their hand wheels setting the steel brake bands on the wildcats. With the ship trembling and the wildcat brakes smoking, the anchor chain—weighing half a ton per fathom—straightened out like a fiddle string pointing down and aft from the hawsepipe.

"That's all we've got, Sir," lied the bosun to the bridge, keeping 30 fathoms up his sleeve as good bosuns usually do. "Chain tends aft—very heavy strain."

"Okay," came the calm reply. "We've got full left rudder on, we'll kill our headway in the swing." The ship was cracking the whip around its anchor now, expending its momentum by ponderously slewing herself sideways through the water while she dragged the mud hook along the bottom.

Finally, when she had swung 90°, the chain, now sticking straight out perpendicular to the side instead of aft, began to relax. The bow eased over toward the anchor and the heavy bight of chain sank to the bottom.

"Aw right, come on back, you guys," growled the bosun. "Heave in to 45 fathoms and secure. A couple of more slam-bang jobs like that and we won't have no wildcat brakes left—or no bosun either maybe."

Down in the engine room the Chief Engineer was also making derogatory comments about the mooring. "The way they jerk that engine-room telegraph handle from 'full astern' to 'stop,' they must think I can turn 100,000 Horse Power on and off like a peanut roaster," he said with an injured air.

"The fire rooms did a mighty fine job, Chief," said the Senior Assistant. "They didn't pop a safety valve when we slammed those throttles closed on them!"

"Yeah—that part was fine," said the Chief. "But it doesn't do the brick work in our furnaces any good to chop all those burners off so sudden. And God knows how many tubes we loosened up in the boilers. Take plenty of time now and cool everything out real slow before you secure."

"Okay Chief—we'll take it easy."

That night in the incinerator compartment on the hangar deck, Fatso and his cronies met for their usual evening repast—and discussion of global strategy.

This evening's strategic discussion hinged on logistics. "She's almost empty, boys," said Fatso, pointing to his sea chest which served as a liquor locker and bar. "We gotta fill her up again while we're here in Naples."

All around the circle, heads nodded in grave agreement with this command decision.

"But we can't bring it aboard by the bottle any more in cardboard boxes," said Satchelaft. "That new ship's order about inspecting all packages brought back from liberty has battened that hatch down."

"Yeah," said Fatso, "a young Ensign OOD in Nice even made *me* heave a package overboard," he added indignantly.

"How about crating up some stuff and having it shipped out here with some of the paymaster's supplies?" asked Scuttlebutt.

"Not with this new paymaster," said Satchelaft. "He sticks that long beak of his into everything. You couldn't even smuggle a needle aboard in his stuff."

"Hey!" said Fatso, eyeing Beer Bottle. "Why can't we ship it out with some of your stuff?"

Beer Bottle was in charge of the "geedunk" shop (soda fountain) and received a shipment of supplies for his soda bar in each port they visited. But he took a dim view of Fatso's proposal. "Nothing doing," he said. "I ain't gonna hold the sack for a deal like that. They'd bust me to WAVE apprentice, if I got caught."

"Now wait a minute, Beer Bottle," said Fatso. "We could work this so you wouldn't have a thing to do with it. I'll handle the whole deal. I'll buy the stuff, arrange to have it delivered on the dock with your gook, and I'll be right here on deck to pick it up when your shipment comes aboard. Even if some nosy guy found it on deck you could honestly say you didn't know nothing about it."

"No," said Beer Bottle. "I won't do it."

But stronger characters than Beer Bottle have been lured from the path of virtue by the wiles of wayward companions. The boys pointed out that after all, he didn't have to *do* anything except keep his mouth shut and fail to notice an extra box in his supplies. He wouldn't be taking any chances at all—Fatso would be the one with his neck out. Eventually Beer Bottle agreed reluctantly and said, "You guys just be sure to pick it up as soon as it gets aboard. I don't want none of that stuff in my storeroom."

"Don't worry about that," said Fatso. "We'll take care of everything. We'll have a special mark on the box so we can pick it out easy—a red cross. The whole deal is in the bag. You can forget all about it."

Fatso might not have been quite so confident about this had he seen the sinister figure standing at that moment outside the incinerator door, his ear to the crack and listening intently. It was his traditional enemy, Commissar Jones. As Commissar tiptoed furtively away he thought to himself, "Now I can put a clove hitch around his fat neck and set taut on it."

But, on second thought, this was not as easy as it seemed. He couldn't just put the finger on Fatso openly and publicly because the ship would get too hot for him to live in if he did. And Fatso's high-level connections made it useless to go to the Skipper or Exec and tip them off on the sly. If a liquor rap were ever officially pinned on Fatso, they would, of course, do their duty and lower the boom on him. But Commissar knew from experience that where Fatso was concerned they might exercise judicious stupidity when necessary and make it hard to pin anything on him.

Soon Commissar's greedy instincts suggested another plan. A case of whiskey that you got for free, if sold by the drink to characters of discretion during a long cruise at sea, would produce a nice profit. And Commissar was not above taking a snifter himself at times. So why not just hijack the stuff? One thing was for sure in a job of that kind; since the whole deal was strictly illegal, just like hijacking operations in prohibition days, your victims couldn't make any official report about it. The more he thought about it, the better Commissar liked this scheme.

Next day Fatso and Beer Bottle went ashore to purchase supplies for the welfare and morale of the *Okinawa*'s crew. On the way uptown from the dock they passed legends painted on walls and fences in red letters three feet high saying, "Amis go home," "Sink Navy Americano."

"Look at those signs," said Beer Bottle, "I don't think these people like us."

"Yeah," said Fatso. "There's a lot of commies here. But most of these Eyetalians are pretty good Joes."

"Well, just make sure that guy you're buying the liquor from is OK and that he's got sense enough not to louse the deal up. I don't mind saying I'm still leary of this thing—there's lots of ways it can backfire and . . ."

"Aw, quit worrying, Beer Bottle," said Fatso. "The way we're working this even a Marine could get away with it."

On this optimistic note the plotters separated and Beer Bottle proceeded to the U.S. Army Commissary, where he placed his order for fifty cases of coca cola, ten boxes of ice cream mix and various other geedunk shop supplies. "Have 'em ready at 0830 tomorrow morning," said Beer Bottle. "I'll have a truck here to take them down to the dock."

Meantime, Fatso sought out a small bottle shop where he was greeted with open arms by the genial proprietor. "Ah, Meester Fatso," he cried. "Long time no see."

"Hiya Tony," said Fatso. "How are all the little bambinos?"

"Ah I gotta one more now," said Tony beaming from ear to ear. "I name him Giovanni Patrico, after you, Meester Fatso."

"Gee," said Fatso, "that's nice. Look, Tony, I want to make a very special deal with you."

"But certainly," said Tony. "I always give my friend Gioninni special price."

Fatso peered cautiously around the shop and noted that it was empty except for a shifty-looking assistant arranging bottles on the shelf.

"I want you to send a case of whiskey out to the ship," he said.

"I send it out in the next boat," said Tony pleasantly.

"No, no Tony," said Fatso. "It is forbidden. I get in bad trouble if they find out. We must do this in a very special way."

Tony raised his eyebrows and shrugged to indicate that nothing American sailors did surprised him very much and said, "You tell me what and I do it."

"Put the bottles in a plain wooden box," said Fatso, "with nothing to show where it came from. Just mark U.S.S. OKINAWA on it and paint a red cross on it so it will look like medical supplies."

Tony laughed heartily at this stratagem.

"Si Signor," said Tony, chuckling to himself over this wonderful plot. Fatso paid for his purchase and departed, not noting the evil leer on the face of Tony's assistant as he shoved off.

That night in a waterfront dive a sinister group met behind bolted doors and drawn blinds, with a tough-looking, bull-necked character presiding. Reporting to the group in hushed tones was Tony's shifty assistant. ". . . and so, many boxes will go aboard ship in the morning. The American dogs are trying to smuggle whiskey on board and will be expecting one box with a red cross on it."

"Comrade," said Bull Neck, "you have done well. Tomorrow we show the Wall Street bullies how the proletariat strikes back. How big is the liquor box?"

"About so," said the assistant indicating. "I have the exact dimensions because I nailed it up myself and put the red cross on it."

"That's big enough," said Bull Neck, "to make very fine explosion. We give the capitalists good service and send extra box out. We must load our box now, with the timer set for 1030 tomorrow morning so it will be down below in the storeroom when it goes off."

"Who will deliver our box?" asked a battered one-eyed character with a peg-leg.

"He will," said Bull Neck, indicating the assistant. "And now, let us get busy Comrades. I want forty sticks of dynamite." It was well after midnight before the conspirators finished their evil task of constructing, loading, and marking the fake liquor box.

When the meeting broke up and comrades slunk off to their hideouts, the peg-leg man made his way, via back alleys, with many furtive glances behind him, to U.S. Army NATO Headquarters, where he requested an audience with the Officer of the Day.

"It's too late—he's gone to bed," said the sergeant on watch, eyeing him disdainfully.

"It is very urgent," said Peg-Leg.

"What is it bub? I'm in charge here and I'll take care of it," said the sergeant.

"I can't tell you sir. I must tell the officer."

"Lissen pal," said the sergeant, "I'm the head man here until the Lieutenant wakes up. If you won't talk to me, you'll have to wait till morning. I ain't going to get chewed out by that shavetail squirt for waking him up now."

You might think that anyone who had such vital information to the national defense as Peg-Leg, involving the safety of a large U.S. Navy aircraft carrier, would have no trouble transmitting it to the U.S. Army. If so, you don't know the Army, and to be fair about it, in this case there was some reason for skepticism. Although Peg-Leg was a trusted undercover agent for G-2, he was a dirty, evil-looking character. He couldn't reveal his identity to the sergeant because his very life depended on confining this knowledge to top-level intelligence officers. No amount of pleading

176

could budge the sergeant, so Peg-Leg settled down to wait.

Out on the *Okinawa* next morning reveille sounded as usual at 0530, while Lieutenants in the Army are still asleep. Soon after reveille, Commissar Jones, checking the plan of the day, noted that a special boat was to pick up geedunk stores from the dock at 0900. Commissar, being a master-at-arms, had no trouble persuading the OOD that he had official business to discuss with the Shore Patrol Officer, and went in to the dock in the 0800 boat, which had instructions to wait and bring him back.

Soon after the boat landed, Tony's communist assistant drove down to the dock in a former U.S. Army jeep and peered cautiously about. Commissar, spotting a crate with a red cross on it in the jeep, walked over and asked, "Who you looking for, my friend?"

The assistant eyed him warily and asked, "You are friend of Tony's friend from American battleship?"

"Yeah," said Commissar, "you got a special package for me?" he asked with a knowing wink.

"Si Signor," said the Comrade. "Shall we wait till the other truckload comes?"

"No," said Commissar, "I'm going to take it aboard myself—it's safer that way," he added mysteriously.

That was good enough for the comrade, who was eager to get rid of his dangerous cargo. Commissar loaded the crate into his boat and, on the way back to the ship, passed the regular stores boat, with Beer Bottle in it, coming in. Arriving at the ship he lugged the crate boldly up the gangway, informed the Officer of the Deck it was stores for the Medical Department, and disappeared below with it. Intending to inspect his loot later, he stowed the deadly box in his locker, and went up to the flight deck to enjoy the sunshine and gloat over his coup.

Promptly at nine o'clock a truck drove down to the dock with the geedunk stores. A few minutes later a smaller truck drove up. Ensconced on the front seat and beaming from ear to ear was Tony.

Now, Hear This!

As Beer Bottle's boys got to work loading the boat, Tony walked over to him, doffed his hat and bowed from the waist. "You are the friend of my friend Giovanno Patrico Gioninni?"he asked.

"Yeah, I know him," said Beer Bottle nervously. "But I got nothing to do with any deal he has with you."

Tony smiled broadly, winked, and made a circle with his thumb and forefinger. Nodding his head toward the liquor crate with the red cross on it just being loaded into the boat he said, "Tony always keeps promises to his friends."

Beer Bottle looked the other way and said, "I don't see nothing but geedunk stores." Soon the boat was loaded and headed back to the ship.

Meantime, as Commissar Jones paced the flight deck at peace with the world, and the clock mechanism ticked away in his locker below, Peg-Leg finally broke through the iron curtain with which Army noncoms protect the brass. Once he did, the Army made up for lost time. The Colonel in G-2 let out a blast of sulphurous language that scorched the Lieutenant duty officer's eyebrows and snarled orders at his cowering staff. As a Major phoned frantically to "Air Operations," the Colonel rushed outside to a waiting jeep and roared off to the airport. By the time he got there, they had a helicopter turning up and in a few minutes he was fluttering out to the *Okinawa*. Plumping down on the flight deck in a blizzard of white hats blown off by his unanticipated arrival, he yelled at the first sailor he saw, who happened to be Commissar Jones, "Take me to the Captain IMMEDIATELY—it's URGENT."

Commissar rushed him down to the cabin and then followed him in protesting when he brushed the Marine orderly out of the way and burst in on the Captain unannounced. "Captain," the Colonel shouted, "the communists sent a bomb aboard your ship this morning—it's in a box with a red cross on it and it's set to explode any minute!"

178

Fatso's Bomb-Disposal Job

When a wild-eyed Colonel comes bursting into the Captain's cabin early in the morning with a crazy tale like this one, a Skipper's first impulse is to send for the senior medico. But anyone smart enough to make Captain realizes immediately that, if the Colonel is nuts, no great harm can be done by humoring him and believing him for a while. If he should turn out to be sane and you *don't* believe him, you could have a disaster on your hands. The Captain grabbed his phone to the Officer of the Deck and said, "This is the Captain. Sound the general alarm—I'll be down on the quarter deck right away." Snatching his cap he said, "Come on, Colonel," and clattered down the ladder to the hangar deck as the general alarm went off.

Commissar Jones had been standing just inside the cabin door with his jaw hanging open and his eyes bugging out while the Colonel was talking. He went down the ladder four jumps ahead of the Captain and raced aft along the hangar deck, knocking sailors out of his way right and left as he went. He disappeared below, ripped open his locker, staggered up on deck with the deadly crate on his shoulder, and heaved it overboard from the fantail. As it sank to the bottom, Commissar sank back on his haunches, mopping his brow, and sat there puffing for a few minutes until it suddenly hit him that this was the worst place on the whole ship to be, when and if that bomb decided to go off.

Meantime, things were happening on the hangar deck.

The Exec rushed up to the Captain with a bewildered look on his face and said, "What's wrong, Sir?"

"Have we taken any stores aboard this morning?" demanded the Skipper.

"Yessir. We just hoisted a cargo net full onto the deck edge elevator."

"Get the damage control party up there right away. There's a bomb in those stores," barked the Skipper. "Come on, Colonel," he said as he headed toward the elevator, dozens of curious officers and men tagging on to the party as they hurried forward.

All this uproar had busted loose as Fatso was about to pick up the liquor crate and lug it back to the incinerator. He was still standing on the deck edge elevator trying to make up his mind whether he should go to his station for what was obviously some cockeyed drill, or if he should take advantage of this chance to get the liquor crate stowed. As the Captain and his entourage hurried toward him, Fatso squared his hat, and started to jog trot toward his drill station. He stopped dead in his tracks as the Colonel yelled, "There it is Cap'n—just like I told you—that one on top of the pile," and he pointed to the box with the red cross on it.

"How do you know that's the one?" demanded the Captain.

"That red cross on it, Sir! Our agent said that's the way it would be marked."

This was like dropping the boat boom on Fatso's head. If he had stopped to think he would have realized that all this excitement couldn't possibly be generated by discovery of a case of liquor on board—not even in the U.S. Navy, which has been bone dry afloat since 1914. But when four-stripe Captains and chicken Colonels are jumping up and down and the whole ship seems to have hit the panic button, you don't always stop to think. Fatso jumped to the conclusion that he had been betrayed—sold out by his good friend Tony, of all people, and now he was caught red-handed in a way that would probably drag poor old Beer Bottle into it too!

"All hands stand back from that elevator," yelled the Executive Officer. "Get that damage control party up here on the double."

Fatso, grasping at straws, saw his chance to at least dispose of the evidence and thus maybe salvage something out of the debacle. As the others fell back from the "deadly" pile, he dashed forward, hoisted the box onto his shoulder, and headed for the outboard edge of the elevator projecting over the side. Now things really became confused. The Colonel hollered, "Look out." The Exec bellowed, "Stand fast," and the Captain yelled, "Let him alone."

In a few seconds Fatso reached the edge and heaved the incriminating evidence overboard.

As the harmless box was sinking to the bottom, the damage control party dashed up arrayed in asbestos suits and rescue breathers, dragging fire hoses and stretchers behind them, and with bomb-disposal experts lugging boxes of special tools. Everyone was just heaving a sigh of relief when the Captain snapped at the Exec, "We got to get away from here—FAST. Get underway immediately and get clear before that damned thing goes off—it's only a few feet from our bottom now!"

"Aye aye Sir," said the Exec and bolted for the nearest phone to the engine room as the Captain headed for the bridge. By the time the Skipper got up there dense black smoke was pouring out of the stack from extra boilers being lit off. He flipped the switch on the squawk box to main engine control and said, "Whaddaya say Chief—How soon can you spin those wheels?"

"We're just lighting off the other boilers now, Cap'n," came the Chief Engineer's reply. "We'll be ready in half an hour."

"Half an hour hell," roared the Captain, "I gotta move right NOW."

"But Captain, we've only got one boiler steaming—it takes at LEAST 20 minutes to raise steam in the rest."

"The hell with the rest of them—we haven't got 20 minutes— what can you do on one boiler?"

"This plant is stone cold, Cap'n—I can't just shoot live steam on cold steel—15 minutes is—"

"Look, Chief—I'm sitting on top of a mine that may go off any minute. I'd rather blow a few gaskets in the engine room than get a hole in my bottom."

"Yessir. Aye Aye Sir! How about getting her moving with one shaft, Sir? I can give you one shaft in about five minutes sir—if nothin' busts," he added dubiously.

The Captain shot a quick look at the wind and tide, noting that it was flat calm and slack water. "Okay Chief," he said. "Let's have all you got on the starboard outboard shaft—I'll wind her around the anchor and swing the ship clear."

Out in the fire rooms, the Chief Water Tender listening in on the circuit put his own interpretation on the Captain's remarks. "My God," he announced, "War has started. The Russians are dropping mines all around us! Pour on the coal, you guys—get them cans boiling."

The Chief Engineer yelled into the fire-room squawk box, "Give me all burners on the steaming boiler. Try to blow the safety valve. I'm going to take the steam away from you faster than you can make it."

Frantic grease-monkeys were leaping around in the starboard engine room opening drain valves, starting oil pumps, and cutting in the main condenser. In the control room the Chief Engineer watched three gages among the dozen on the master panel—main steam, vacuum, and oil pressure in #1 engine room. As soon as the Vacuum and oil pressure pointers came off their pegs and started to rise he yelled, "Stand by out there in #1, it's coming to you red hot." Turning to the young sailor with both hands on a big brass wheel he said, "Okay son. Crack your throttle on #1. Pull your main steam down to 600 pounds and then hold it there with your wheel."

As the steam hissed through the throttle valve and hit the cold engine room pipes, slugs of condensed water pounded through the lines making all engineers cringe and wince at the outrage being committed on their plant. In #1 engine room, all hands held their breath as the hot steam shot into the stationary cold turbine rotor.

On a gamble like this you win or lose in the first half-minute. If you get the rotor spinning, it will warm up and expand evenly all around, even though much more quickly than the book allows. But if she sticks, with that hot high-pressure steam shooting through, you can warp it out of shape and strip the blades. The #1 high pressure turbine shuddered, groaned, blew steam out of both glands, and began to spin.

In the main control room the Chief noted the revolution counter kicking over and said, "Aw right now, son, watch that main steam gage. Don't pull it below 550. Just play with that throttle and we'll take whatever RPM we can get." Then flipping the switch to the bridge he reported smugly, "We're making 40 turns on #1 shaft, Cap'n— nothing has let go *yet*, Sir."

On the bridge the Captain said, "Tell the foc'sle to veer out chain to the bitter end, and then hold everything. I'm going to swing the ship around the hook." Walking over to the wing of the bridge he fixed his gaze on a piece of driftwood alongside in the water and noted that the ship was beginning to inch ahead. It takes 60,000 tons some time to gain headway and a four-screw ship never will go very fast on one. The *Okinawa* forged ponderously ahead taking the slack out of her anchor chain, and in a few minutes she had straightened out the chain and was straining at the end of it. With the port anchor down and the starboard shaft kicking ahead, she began to pivot around the anchor with the stern swinging slowly to starboard. After five minutes she had swung 90° and the entire hull was well clear of the water in which the infernal machine was resting.

Suddenly there was a muffled underwater explosion, the ship trembled as if she had hit a rock, and a pillar of muddy water shot 30 feet up in the air about 200 yards on the port quarter.

The Captain mopped his brow, turned to the Exec and said, "Tell the foc'sle to heave in to 45 fathoms and secure." Then walking over to the engine room squawk box, he called down, "Okay Chief, you can relax now. Secure and set the auxiliary watch. Well done to all hands in the Black Gang."

Up to this point Fatso, like most others on the ship, had little idea what all the excitement was about. Rumors were flying thick and fast all over the hangar deck, some coming down from the bridge and others up from the fire rooms—"Commie frogmen trying to stick limpet mines on the bottom." "Russian submarine in the harbor." "That splash astern was from a bomb dropped by a plane flying so high you couldn't even see it."

Twenty years of sea duty had taught Fatso that strange things happen in the Navy, but they all count on thirty-year retirement, so he didn't worry too much about them. But despite all this extra whoop-de-doo, Fatso still thought somebody had squealed about his smuggling enterprise. He was just congratulating himself that this cockeyed "drill" had taken the spotlight off him when squawk boxes all over the ship blared the word, "Now hear this, Gioninni, bosun's mate first class, report to the Captain on the bridge."

That brought him up with a round turn. On the way to the bridge, he decided there was no use trying to bluff his way out of this, and maybe get Beer Bottle involved too. When confronted by the Captain, he would simply make a clean breast of things and shoulder all blame himself.

"You sent for me, Sir?" said Fatso, saluting the Captain sheepishly when he got up to the bridge.

The Captain grinned from ear to ear, stuck out his hand and said, "Congratulations and thanks, Gioninni—that was a very brave thing you did."

"Whu—wh—what did you say, Sir?" asked Fatso.

"Your conduct was in accordance with the best traditions of the U.S. Navy," said the Captain pumping his hand up and down.

This wasn't according to script at all. But Fatso had an emergency procedure for handling such situations which has often made bigger wheels than him look good—he just put on a wise look and made evasive, noncommittal comments.

"Yessir—yessir—I mean, that is—Aw heck, Sir."

"You prevented a disaster by heaving that bomb overboard and I'm going to see that you get a medal for it."

"Aw—anyone else would of done the same thing," said Fatso

modestly.

"You're still the same old Fatso you used to be on the *Lexington*," said the Captain, waxing sentimental.

"You don't know the half of it, Cap'n," said Fatso, with much more truth than poetry.

Going back to the incinerator, Fatso met Commissar Jones on the hangar deck. Commissar was still shook by that trip to the stern with the bomb on his shoulder, but he had already concocted a tale explaining how he had spotted the bomb and was on his way to the bridge to tell it to the Captain and receive due credit for it. "What did they want you on the bridge for, Gioninni?" he asked.

"I don't understand all I know about it *yet*," said Fatso. "But the Old Man got me up there to thank me for heaving a bomb overboard—says he's going to get me a medal for it."

Commissar stood rooted to the deck for some seconds, completely flabbergasted, his jaws flapping up and down but no words coming out. When words finally did erupt, they indicated a deplorable lack of faith in the essential justice of life on this earth.

⚓ CHAPTER TEN

Patent Medicine

As THE OKINAWA steamed into the fading Mediterranean twilight, the bosun's mate of the watch on the bridge flipped a row of switches on the loudspeaker control box and blew a long shrill blast on his pipe. Squawk boxes all over the ship repeated the blast and passed the word, "Now hear this: On deck the first section . . . relie-e-e-ve the wheel and lookouts . . . lay up to the bridge all the 8 o'clock reports . . . the watch and lifeboat crew of the watch to muster." It was ten minutes to 8 bells of the second dog watch, time for the next watch to be relieving.

Soon the oncoming watch-standers were trooping up through the island to their stations: signal floozies, orderlies, messengers, lookouts, quartermasters, and all the others that it takes to man the sea detail of a large aircraft carrier. Masters-at-arms and section leaders made their inspections and came up to the bridge to report "All secure."

An alert young Ensign with binoculars around his neck marched briskly onto the hushed, dimly lighted bridge, banged his heels together, saluted the Officer of the Deck, and said, "Sir, I am ready to relieve you." The Ensign was only two years out of the

186

Academy, had already qualified for top watch underway, and was justifiably pleased with himself.

The OOD, a Lieutenant, said tolerantly, "Okay, Pinky. We are on course 270 true, 272 magnetic, 275 per standard compass. Standard speed is 12 knots with four boilers on the line. Radar has a target on the screen up ahead on opposite course one point on the port bow—it isn't in sight yet. Point Largo light will . . . etc., etc." For the next five minutes he rattled through the time-honored ritual of the sea for turning over the deck—all very official.

Meantime, the new helmsman took over the wheel a bit more informally. He tiptoed softly up behind the sailor he was to relieve, peered over his shoulder at the gyro compass, and then goosed him in the stern sheets and said quietly, "Okay Jinglebells. Whassa dope?"

"Ooops—steering two seven zero, you sonofabitch," said Jinglebells. "And she's carrying about three degrees of right rudder to hold her on."

Up on the lookout platform one sailor handed his battle phone and binoculars over to his relief and said, "Nothing in sight now, but radar claims there's a ship one point on the port bow coming this way. You better keep your eyes open and pick her up before the bridge does. That Ensign who's trying to make Admiral has the next watch."

"Okay Mac—I got her."

On the stroke of eight bells the Ensign saluted again and said, "Sir, I relieve you," thereby promoting himself (in authority and responsibility) for the next four hours over the heads of everyone on the ship except the Captain. "Messenger," he barked, "report to the Captain it's eight bells, watch is relieved, eight o'clock lights and galley fires out, prisoners secure."

So the *Okinawa* settled down for a calm evening of routine cruising.

Down in the incinerator compartment Fatso sat on a bucket

Now, Hear This!

staring pensively into the firebox of his big trash furnace where a mess of bacon and eggs was sizzling. "If you guys don't figure out how to raise some money pretty quick," said Fatso, "we might as well be headed for Alaska next week instead of the Riviera." Beer Bottle, Satchelaft and Scuttlebutt, also seated on buckets staring into the furnace, nodded sadly in agreement.

Tonight they were discussing the forthcoming visit to Nice, and viewing it with alarm because they were all broke.

"When we were in Nice for the 4th of July," said Beer Bottle, "the Mayor made a speech about how we had liberated France from the Huns and won their eternal gratitude."

"Yeah," said Fatso. "And for that—plus a couple of hundred francs—they'll sell you a cuppa coffee."

"For a couple of hundred more they'll sell you their grandmother," observed Satchelaft.

"Who cares about their *grandmother?* But get 'em a little younger and—"

At this moment the ship's loudspeaker boomed out with the regular evening newscast. "Good evening shipmates, this is Itchy McGonigle in the radio shack broadcasting the news of the world hot from home. New York—Today the United Nations . . ."

"Turn the volume down on that squawk box," growled Fatso. "We got more important things to think about. When we get to Nice next week we've gotta have dough—or else we'll make our liberty from the bridge through the spy glass."

"Why can't we run another anchoring pool," demanded Satchelaft. "We made two hundred bucks off that one in Naples."

"Not a chance," said Fatso. "The Exec called me in and lowered the boom on me for that. He says no more gambling pools period."

"Well, why not run one anyway?" demanded Satchelaft belligerently.

"Nothing doing," said Fatso. "I got an understanding with the Commander that he will let me run this incinerator, if I let him run the rest of the ship. It's been working out pretty good so far, and I don't want to have no trouble with the Commander."

During the silence which followed this statement, the news broadcast continued, ". . . a sensational new patent medicine called Caracol has the whole United States excited with a spectacular sales campaign. A caravan of movie stars now touring the country making one-night stands is selling the stuff faster than they can bottle it. The American Medical Association says . . ."

"Now if I just had the concession for that stuff on this ship," observed Beer Bottle, "I could clean up enough in the next few days for all of us to make the biggest liberty of the cruise in Nice."

"Don't kid yourself," said Satchelaft. "The guys on this ship have been around. They aren't like those suckers in small towns back home—they wouldn't fall for that racket, would they Fatso?"

"I dunno," said Fatso judicially, "some of the draft dodgers that we're getting in the Navy nowadays are pretty dumb. We put a suit of blues on 'em, sprinkle salt over 'em, and tell them they're sailors. But most of them can't pour water out of a boot when the directions are on the heel." Other seafarers present indicated general agreement with Fatso's low estimate of the current crop of naval volunteers.

"I was a pitch man with a carnival the first three years after I ran away from home," said Beer Bottle. "Used to sell 'Mother's Miracle Pain Killer' to young and old, rich and poor. I'll bet I could sell bust-developing salve to this crew of inland yokels."

Beer Bottle ran the "geedunk" shop on the *Okinawa* and was regarded as an expert on merchandising and business administration by other members of Fatso's clique.

"Business principles are simple, and once you learn them you can get rich selling anything," he added pontifically.

"Okay, professor," said Fatso. "Explain these principles to us ignorant sailors here."

"Well," began Beer Bottle, "take production for instance. You gotta sell your product cheap, so you've got to make it even cheaper. That's all there is to the Ford Motor Company's operation. The best way to make a thing cheap is to make it out of something you get for free."

"Uh huh," said Fatso skeptically, "if you can pick it off the bushes for free, how do you get people to pay good money for it?"

"I'm coming to that," said Beer Bottle. "You do something to the stuff you pick off the bushes to make it seem different. But you shouldn't run your production cost up doing it, otherwise your inventory ties up all your operating capital—in other words, the nut on the deal gets too big. Then, of course, there's no use making a lot of stuff that you can sell at a fair price unless people are going to want it. That's where advertising comes in. You've got to create a demand for your product."

"So how do you create the demand, Beer Bottle? Issue a ship's order about it?" asked Fatso.

"One good way is to get people worrying about something and then sell them a medicine that will make them quit worrying—like those ads you see in newspapers and magazines about people who got bad breath or who stink when they sweat. You get people thinking about something like that and then sell 'em a pill or a lotion to make them think they smell sweet again—I made a good living doing that for three years before I shipped in this Navy."

"The only way to worry the guys on this ship," observed Satchel-aft, "is to tell them there ain't gonna be no liberty in the next port because an epidemic has busted out there or something."

"That wouldn't do us any good," said Beer Bottle. "But, if we got a rumor going that an epidemic had started in the port we just *left*, that they had been exposed to it, and that we had a cure for it—maybe that would."

"Yeah," agreed Fatso. "Suppose we got word around that cholera had just busted out in Naples. Then we could sell everybody cholera pills—"

"Naw. That's too crude," said Beer Bottle. "Besides, everybody on board has had cholera shots and, if you get them worried about something real serious like dying, they'll go down to sick bay and see the Senior Medico. You gotta be subtle. You just want to worry them—not scare the ears off of them."

"Okay," said Fatso, "so suppose we got everybody worrying, what do we sell them to make 'em quit worrying?"

"Oh-h-h—almost anything," said Beer Bottle. "It could be pills, salve, or liquid, so long as it's harmless and easy to get. Liquid stuff is easiest to make. You could sell sea water if you dress it up a little bit. Of course you got a packaging problem there. But I got a storeroom half-full of empty Coca Cola bottles, so let's say it's a liquid—we gotta make this stuff look official and sort of antiseptic like—what's the name of that new drug they claim is good for whatever ails you these days?—they put it in tooth paste and it comes out green."

"You mean chlorophyll?" asked Fatso.

"Yeah, chlorophyll, that's it," said Beer Bottle. "We'll make this stuff of ours green and call it Chlorocol."

"So now we got a thousand bottles of green medicine," said Satchelaft. "What are we going to do with it? Nobody on this ship is worried about nothing. Nobody knows about our stuff and we got no way of advertising it—unless Fatso can persuade his pal the Exec to make an announcement about it at quarters—"

"Oh yes we have," said Beer Bottle. "We got old Itchy McGonigle and his daily news broadcast. We can have him slip in a phony item to get everybody worrying. On this ship Itchy corresponds to a nationwide hookup back home of CBS, NBC, and all the rest of them put together. Here comes the great commentator himself now," added Beer Bottle as Itchy entered the furnace room.

"Well boys, how did you like my broadcast tonight?" asked Itchy.

Now, Hear This!

"Didn't hear it Bub—we tuned you out to talk about more important things."

"What's more important than news of the world?" demanded Itchy indignantly.

"Spending money for sailors on the Riviera," said Fatso. "Look, Itchy, we got a big deal cooking—who checks up on what you say on your broadcasts?"

"Nobody checks up on me," said Itchy righteously. "We got free speech and freedom of the press on this ship just like back home. And besides they don't have to check up on me. All my stuff comes right off the Armed Forces broadcast. If I put out any bum dope don't blame me—"

"Keep your shirt on, Itchy. Nobody said you been putting out any bum dope, but how about sticking in a little item for us on your next couple of broadcasts?"

"You mean a phony? I wouldn't think of doing anything like that," said Itchy piously, "unless there was some good reason for it."

"There's a very fine reason," said Fatso. "Right now we're all broke. If you go along with us on this we can have buckets full of money by the time we hit the Riviera."

"What's the pitch?" asked Itchy eagerly.

"You just tack an item on the end of tomorrow morning's broadcast about an epidemic in Naples, that's all."

"What kind of epidemic? They got every disease known to medical science in Naples. The whole town is an epidemic if you ask me."

So Fatso explained the broad outlines of their scheme and the gang sat around till late that night conspiring on the details, and planning to produce, advertise, and sell whatever Beer Bottle put in his Coca Cola bottles. Moe Ginsberg, dental technician second class, volunteered to be Beer Bottle's medical adviser and to see that the stuff he concocted was not poisonous. Itchy was to be advertising manager for the venture, and Fatso agreed to sell the product in the incinerator room and handle finances. Beer Bottle undertook to produce and deliver twenty cases of salable merchandise during the morning watch.

By one bell of the mid watch the operation plan was completed, while the *Okinawa* cruised leisurely past the Barbary Coast bound for the sunny Côte d'Azur in France.

Next morning at 0700, Itchy rattled off the news of the day in his usual brisk manner. At the end of his regular ten-minute period he flipped the switches in the radio shack that cut out the squawk boxes in the officers' country and in sick bay and continued:

"Naples, Italy. Public-health authorities are baffled by a strange disease which broke out along the waterfront here this week and is spreading to other parts of the city. Victims feel normal in all respects and have no symptoms except their teeth become loose and, in many cases, fall out. Doctors and dentists are struggling to check this disease, which is rapidly reaching epidemic proportions. It is spread by knives and forks in restaurants, by bar glasses, and by kissing. First loosening of teeth occurs ten days after exposure."

This news hit the *Okinawa* like an atom bomb. Everybody had eaten a few meals ashore in Naples, some had hoisted more than a few drinks, and Neapolitan gals are very demonstrative. So practically all hands figured they had been exposed one way or another during the recent visit to Naples.

A big ship at sea is the best rumor factory in the world, and by noon all sorts of wild tales were circulating: "Fifty cases of it already on the *Okinawa*" . . . "A guy up in the first division had all his teeth come out when he started to brush them this morning" . . . "The Dental Officer says the best thing to do is to pull them all out as soon as they get loose," etc., etc. Fatso and his cohorts kept hearing such rumors all day long and perhaps the reason was because they kept spreading them.

Now, Hear This!

They also appeared frequently during the day in the various washrooms around the ship and gargled green colored liquid from Coca Cola bottles. When asked what this stuff was they replied vaguely, "It's some medicine Moe Ginsberg in the Dental Office mixes up out of Chlorophyll that he swiped from the medical storeroom . . . it stops that Naples disease."

That night Itchy's broadcast said, "Epidemic still raging in Naples. Doctors have discovered disease can be detected in early stages by tapping on your teeth with a pencil. If tapping produces a hollow sound instead of the usual solid tone, you have the disease. They are now experimenting with the new wonder drug Chlorophyll, which seems to check the disease if used soon enough."

Before taps that night nearly all hands had tried tapping on their teeth with a pencil and most of them decided that the sound produced was hollow. Meantime, rumors continued to fly and word flashed from stem to stern and from bilges to the upper signal bridge that Fatso was selling a Chlorophyll medicine that killed the disease bugs.

Next morning right after reveille, a long line of men formed outside the incinerator compartment to buy Chlorocol at two bits a bottle. Sailors the world over have more confidence in merchandise they pay for than in similar stuff issued free by the government —especially if there is something shady about the deal by which they acquire the non-regulation stuff. And besides, word soon got around that the dumb Senior Medical Officer didn't even know about the epidemic in Naples and had given several guys the brushoff when they went down to sick bay with their teeth. Fatso sold out his whole supply before breakfast that morning and had to send Beer Bottle a rush order for another consignment of twenty cases.

"Reminds me of when I was a kid back in Tennessee," remarked Beer Bottle to Satchelaft as they filled more bottles with the won-

194

der drug that morning. "I used to help my pappy making whiskey. He made the best corn likker in Cumberland County—but business was never as good as this!"

"What's going to happen if some ear-banger finds out about this and goes running to one of the officers with the dope on it?"

"All they could possibly do is make us knock off selling it," said Beer Bottle judicially. "We don't make any claims for this stuff at all—a demand sprang up for it and all we do is just supply the demand; it's a public service and helps keep up the morale of the crew."

"How about these bottles?" asked Satchelaft. "Aren't they government property?"

"I should say not," said Beer Bottle. "They're *my* property."

"How come?" asked Satchelaft.

"The Paymaster charges enough for cokes to cover the cost of the bottle and to make his regular profit for the government too. So when you buy a coke at my geedunk shop you really buy bottle and all."

"Then why the hell do we have to turn the bottles back in?" demanded Satchelaft indignantly.

"You don't really *have* to," said Beer Bottle craftily. "You guys just think you do. You could throw the bottles overboard if you wanted to. But when you *give* them back to me, I save 'em to turn in ashore for two cents apiece, myself—it would be wasteful if I didn't."

For the next three days business boomed at Fatso's apothecary shop. Nearly everybody on the ship gargled faithfully many times a day. Beer Bottle was kept busy brewing new batches of Chlorocol, and nobody's teeth fell out, much to the relief of those sailors who had made especially big liberties in Naples.

Some men showed up at sick bay each morning to check up on their teeth, thereby puzzling the Medical Officers, who still hadn't got the word about Itchy's broadcasts. Eventually the Medicos decided these men were trying to work some kind of malingering racket, and began prescribing large doses of castor oil for the teeth cases. This was all grist for Fatso's mill and by the fourth day over $500.00 was in his treasury and money was rolling in merrily.

But then, as so often happens ashore when a thriving new commercial venture gets started, greed reared its ugly head. One morning on the hangar deck Fatso met Chief Pharmacist's Mate "Honest John" Binks. Binks pulled him over into a corner and said, "Fatso, my friend, I was on my way down to see you—you know I've always liked you, don't you?"

"Yeah," said Fatso cautiously. As is often the case with people whose nickname is "Honest," Binks was an unsavory character. Fatso didn't trust him any further than he could spit into the wind.

"I'd certainly hate to see you get in any trouble, Fatso," said Honest John.

"That's nice and shipmatey of you," said Fatso, "and I appreciate it. But I ain't in trouble and I don't aim to get into none."

"How's business these days?" asked Honest John.

"Oh, about as usual," said Fatso vaguely. "One day's trash is about the same as another's in the incinerator."

"How about this patent-medicine racket you got?"

Fatso knew a storm warning when he saw one. Binks' query foretold trouble just as surely as when a shore patrol officer casually asks a sailor to see his liberty card.

"Well—what about it?" said Fatso.

"Don't you think you ought to cut me in?" asked Honest John.

"Why?" demanded Fatso indignantly.

"Making medicine comes under my department," said the Chief Pharmacist's Mate. "You've got a pretty nice proposition there. I think I ought to get my cut on it—say about twenty-five bucks a day."

This was blackmail—a seagoing version of the protection racket. Fatso reacted to it the same way that many another honest businessman ashore has done when hoodlums try to muscle in and prey on the fruits of his own individual thrift, enterprise and initiative.

"Nuts," he said.

"Don't get too independent, my friend," said Honest John. "All I'm trying to do is to keep you out of trouble—But if you can't see it that way, that's your tough luck."

"There's nothing wrong about what I'm doing," said Fatso. "But I'll fold it up before I cut you in on it."

"Oh yeah? Of course, all you're doing is mixing and distributing drugs on a U.S. naval vessel—that's a serious offense, like practicing medicine without a license. If I was to make out a report against you for that . . ."

Fatso made a highly impracticable suggestion as to what Honest John could do with any report slip he made out.

"All right, wise guy—you'll be sorry," said Honest John, and the interview ended on that somewhat ominous note. Fatso dismissed the matter from his mind and went on about his business, which was mostly handing out bottles and making change for dollar bills.

But late that afternoon the boom was suddenly lowered on him when the Executive Officer's orderly appeared at the incinerator and told Fatso the Commander wanted to see him immediately. In any military organization, when a big wheel sends for a very small one, it's like a summons from the principal's office for a kid in school. On the way up to the Commander's cabin, Fatso reviewed his conduct for the past month and had alibis ready for those deeds most likely to be the cause of this summons.

In a situation of this kind Fatso wouldn't dream of imposing upon the firm and long-standing friendship between him and the Exec. Outside the cabin he uncovered, snapped to attention, and announced, "Gioninni, bosun's mate first class, sir—you sent for me, sir?"

Now, Hear This!

"Yes. Come in. What's this I hear about you peddling medicine on the hangar deck?" the Commander demanded with forced severity.

"What medicine do you mean, sir?" asked Fatso innocently.

"This green stuff," said the Commander pointing to a bottle on the desk.

"Oh *that* stuff," said Fatso. "Well, it depends on what you been hearing, Commander!"

"For one thing, I hear you are selling it under false pretenses."

"That ain't so, Commander," said Fatso. "We—I mean, I don't make any pretenses or claims at all. For some reason or another everybody on the ship wants this stuff and I just supply it, that's all. You know how crazy rumors get around on a ship Commander, and the boys get funny ideas sometimes—"

The Commander nodded that he knew. "You mean you don't claim this is a medicine?"

"That's right. I don't make any claims at all, honest I don't, Commander."

The Commander knew from long experience that when Fatso had to lie in a matter of this kind he didn't do it in such a straightforward and unequivocal manner. "Well, maybe I'm wrong about that angle," he said. "Let's drop that part of the business"—and Fatso grinned appreciatively. "There are more serious things involved. What is this stuff? Where do you get it?"

"We—I mean I make it," said Fatso, "from a secret formula."

"I want to know what's in it," said the Commander.

"Nothing that can hurt anybody," said Fatso. "It's just a gargle. It don't taste very good, but even if you swallow it, it won't hurt you any more than a mouthful of sea water."

"What gives it that green color?"

Actually Fatso didn't know, but there was no use complicating things by saying so. "You've heard of that new drug chlorophyll, haven't you sir? It cures almost anything. It's green, and everybody

198

knows about it, so I decided to make this stuff green too."

The Commander drew unwarranted conclusions from Fatso's answer.

"So it *is* chlorophyll, is it?" he demanded with a new note of gravity in his voice. "The Chief Pharmacist's Mate reports that six packages of chlorophyll have been stolen from his storeroom and that you are using it to make this stuff."

This charge caught Fatso flat-footed. He had no idea what they were using for coloring matter, but he never dreamed that old timers like Beer Bottle and Ginsberg would commit such a serious offense as stealing government property—at least, not so stupidly.

"Well now, I didn't *say* that I'm using chlorophyll, Commander," said Fatso, stalling for time. "I never stole government property in my whole life—"

"Not if it was bolted to the deck and guarded by a Marine," observed the Commander. "Now look Gioninni—I can't believe you stole it either. But this is a matter of record now. An official report has been made and I've got to take action on it. There must be others in on this deal with you and maybe one of them did it without your knowledge. If you help me straighten this out—and if your skirts are clean, I'll see to it that you don't get hurt."

The Commander probably knew he wasn't going to get anywhere on that tack. Fatso followed that school of naval leadership which believes in loyalty down as well as up. Flogging and keelhauling couldn't drag the names of his accomplices out of him.

"Nobody else is in on it, sir. I done it all myself."

"You mean you stole the Chlorophyll too?" asked the Commander.

"I didn't say that, sir. I didn't steal anything—but I'm the only one involved in this thing, sir."

"Okay, Gioninni," said the Exec. "If you want to be a martyr I can't stop you. But as things stand now you're on the report for stealing chlorophyll. You'll have to be at mast before the Captain tomorrow."

"Aye aye, Sir," said Fatso.

Fatso was a badly worried man when he left the Exec's cabin. A lot of things can happen to well-intentioned sailors at mast and Fatso knew from previous experience that most of them were bad. But when Beer Bottle heard what the charges were, he said, "This is a push-over, Fatso. We'll make that guy Honest John look so silly they'll bust him to Hospitalman Apprentice . . ."

Next day Fatso lined up with the other offenders on the starboard side of the flight deck facing the rostrum set up near the island for the Captain to hold mast. On one side of the rostrum was the Chief Master-At-Arms with the report slips, a yeoman with the service records of the culprits, and various witnesses, most of them reluctant ones. On the other were the Chaplain, the Division Officers of the accused, the Legal Officer and various others whose duty it was to assist the Captain in dispensing naval justice, impartially protecting the rights of both the United States and its citizens in naval uniform. As the Captain and Exec emerged from the island and strode to the rostrum, the CMAA barked, "Mast cases right-hand SALUTE . . . TWO!"

"First case, Seaman Pettybone, Cap'n—charged with inciting a riot in a foreign port, resisting arrest, and beating up six Eyetalian policemen."

A skinny redheaded sailor about five feet high with a black eye, a battered face, and a swollen jaw, stepped forward and uncovered to answer these charges.

The Captain heard the evidence against him, listened to a wonderful tale from Pettybone "explaining" the whole business, and took action on the case as dictated by his conscience, the weight of evidence, the demands of military law, and the past record of the accused.

Fatso's case, being the most serious one that morning, was called last. As Fatso took his place on the hot spot and uncovered, the Chief Master-at-Arms read from the report slip:

"Theft of government property—and unauthorized dispensing of drugs."

Chief Pharmacist's Mate Honest John Binks related that six packages of chlorophyll were missing from his storeroom. He produced his inventory sheets to prove it. He told how right after the drugs disappeared Cioninni began selling large quantities of chlorophyll solution. He introduced a bottle of the offending solution in evidence and called attention to its telltale green color. He pointed out that Chlorophyll was a new drug not obtainable ashore anywhere in the Mediterranean, nor could it be bought by mail from the U.S. The only possible source of supply was the medical store room.

Next the Senior Medical Officer testified that the properties of this chlorophyll solution were unknown, it had never been properly tested by the medical profession, and its use as a gargle might be dangerous. Furthermore, it was intolerable for laymen who knew nothing about medicine to be mixing and dispensing powerful drugs . . .

"Cap'n, may I ask the doctor a question?" said Fatso respectfully.

"Go ahead."

"Doctor," said Fatso, "is salt water dangerous to gargle?"

"Certainly not," said the Doctor. "A saline solution is about the best gargle I know of. It's good for sore throat and trench mouth. It helps the ethmoidal and sphenoidal sinuses. It's used intravenously in some postoperative treatment and it's even given intraperitonally to children who lack fluids."

"How about ordinary sea water? Is that good too?" asked Fatso.

"Well—not as good as a proper solution prepared by a regular physician, but it couldn't possibly do any harm and *might* do some good."

"That's all this stuff of mine is, Cap'n," said Fatso. "Mostly sea water. A lot of the boys are worrying about their teeth for some reason or another since we left Naples, and they think this stuff is good for them."

"By the way, Doctor," said the Captain, "what are we doing to protect our people from this Naples disease?" (Itchy had forgotten to cut out the squawk box on the signal bridge right outside the Captain's sea cabin—so the Skipper had heard all his broadcasts.)

"What Naples disease?" asked the Medico.

"This dental epidemic that they're having there."

"I—well, er—that is, I haven't heard anything about an epidemic there sir," said the Medico in some confusion.

"What?!? You mean to say you haven't done anything to protect the crew? Well—we'll go into that later," said the Captain. Getting back to Fatso he resumed, "Now, how about this chlorophyll business. If you are using stolen drugs to color this stuff, it's a serious offense even if the concoction is harmless."

"Cap'n," said Fatso, "if you'll give me permission to make some of my gargle right here, I'll prove I'm innocent in half a minute."

"Go ahead," said the Skipper.

At a signal from Fatso, Beer Bottle came out from behind the island carrying a bucket of sea water and an aviator's life jacket with the little package of powder attached that makes a big brilliant colored stain in the water to assist in finding downed airmen. Fatso pulled open the flap over the dye marker pocket and dropped a few grains of powder into the bucket. The water in the bucket immediately turned a brilliant green.

"There she is Cap'n," said Fatso. "That stuff in the bottle is just plain sea water with a leetle pinch of green dye marker—The doctor says it's good for you."

There was an embarrassed pause while officers' eyes popped on one side of the rostrum and sailors struggled to suppress budding grins on the other.

This was broken by the ship's Legal Officer, T. Tuttle Taylor, who said, "Of course, even that dye marker is government property, Captain. The Supreme Court has ruled—"

"That stuff I used came out of a life jacket that was sent up to the incinerator to be burned," said Fatso.

"Case dismissed," said the Captain.

Right after mast the Exec had a few quick man-to-man words with Fatso and then went to see the Captain. In a few moments he was able to persuade the Captain that the Senior Medico had *not* been remiss in his duties, and that the only thing to do in this case was to stop the sale of Chlorocol and then sweep the whole business under the rug.

A few days later Fatso bumped into Honest John Binks on the hangar deck. "Hello Chief," said Fatso. "Did you ever find that missing chlorophyll, pal?"

"Yeah," said the Chief, "it's a funny thing, but I did. That dumb second class of mine just stowed those six packages on the wrong shelf and—"

"Uh huh," said Fatso. "You know Binks, dumb clucks like me are kinda glad to see guys like you make chief."

"How come?"

"It means there's hope for all of us to make it!"

⚓ CHAPTER ELEVEN

Trouble at Mardi Gras

As THE OKINAWA steamed easily through the balmy Mediterranean, a "Happy Hour" was in progress on the hangar deck. The forward elevator, lowered to a few feet above hangar-deck level, served as the stage, with the elevator well-framed by faces and white hats of sailors lying prone on the flight deck under the stars and peering into the theater below. Officers and men jammed the hangar deck itself. Half the sailors were seated on mess benches lugged up from the deck below, and the rest ensconced on airplane wings, ladders to the flight deck, the catwalks, and the great athwartship beams supporting the flight deck. All were in a relaxed mood after a week of operations at sea.

A crew of 3,000 sailors can always produce entertainers of varied talents, and their shipmates are the most vocal and uninhibited dramatic critics in the world. This show featured singers, dancers, jugglers, and acrobats, and at the end of each act pandemonium broke loose on the hangar deck. Sometimes it was applause and sometimes raspberries, but the Okinawa's escorting destroyers, 2,000 yards away, had no difficulty telling which acts were hits and which ones "stunk up the joint."

One act was a dramatic skit with several female characters, including a benevolent old lady played with great skill and realism by Satchelaft. As the grand finale wound up the show the Chief Master-At-Arms bellowed for all hands to stand fast while the Captain said a few words.

The Old Man, well liked by all hands, was greeted by cheers, whistles and applause. He announced that the next port of call would be Nice, arriving in time for the Mardi Gras. He hoped that all hands would enjoy themselves *but*—and then came a five-minute pep talk on behavior ashore in foreign ports, particularly Nice, where there had been some recent unpleasant incidents. He said that in any encounter with the police, sailors should never put up an argument, but should treat the cop as if he were the Old Man himself. This, he added, was especially important in foreign ports where our sailors were supposed to be ambassadors of good will by whom the local population judged the whole United States.

When the Old Man finished, a dead silence resounded through the hangar deck. He had touched on a sore spot.

On the way up to the cabin country he remarked to the Admiral, "I'm afraid I smell trouble brewing in Nice, Sir."

"It's been brewing a long time," replied the Admiral, "and the French have been asking for it."

"Can't we do something about it, Sir? The police are working an organized racket on us there. I hate to put my lads ashore where we *know* they're going to get in trouble."

"So do I," said the Admiral. "I've beefed about this situation to the Ambassador a number of times. But he's too busy with his social duties to bother about it."

"Why do we keep coming back there? The fleet must spend four or five million dollars a year in Nice. If we stayed away for a while, the local merchants would raise Cain and make the civil authorities straighten the cops out in a hurry."

Now, Hear This!

"I've tried to pull our ships out of Nice, but the State Department won't hold still for it. They make me keep one big ship in there all the time . . . claim they can't afford to hurt the feelings of our gallant French allies."

"What I'm worrying about is hurting my sailors," said the Captain, as they arrived at the door of the Admiral's cabin. "Well—good night, Sir—see you in the morning."

As the ship's company headed for the bunk rooms to crawl into their sacks, the group of salty characters presided over by Fatso met in the incinerator compartment.

"That was a good show tonight," remarked Scuttlebutt as the clan gathered.

"Yeah," replied Fatso, "and in that skit they put on, old Satchelaft looked a lot more like a nice old lady than my grandmother does."

"He was good all right," said Beer Bottle. "But of all the characters on this ship, Satch would of been the last guy I'd pick to play an old lady. He may be small and frail looking—but remember how he beat up those four French cops last time we were in Nice?"

They remembered, and all faces lit up like lighthouses.

"I wonder," said Scuttlebutt, "if the Old Man really believed that stuff he dished out tonight about being good little sailors when we go ashore in Nice?"

"Not by a bucketful he didn't," said Fatso. "He's been out of boot camp longer than any three of us put together. He knows what those French cops have been doing to us. But he's got to get up and give that song and dance just the same."

"Did you guys hear what happened to the *Salem* in Nice last week?" demanded Satchelaft. "The last night they were in port the gendarmes pinched over fifty of the boys and fined them 20,000 francs apiece."

"20,000 francs!!" said Beer Bottle. "I wouldn't pay it!"

"Oh yes you would," said Fatso, "if the ship was sailing the next day and that was the only way you could get out of jail. These cops always wait till the last night to pull their racket because they know the boys have to get back, and besides all the local shopkeepers would get sore about hurting trade if they did it sooner."

"When we were in there last 4th of July," said Beer Bottle, "the Mayor made a speech about how we had liberated France from the Huns and won their eternal gratitude."

"Yeah," said Fatso. "But these Frenchmen are used to getting something for nothing from Uncle Sugar. They figure they're being gypped if a sailor has any money at all left when he leaves port. So the cops see to it that he doesn't have."

"They fine you just for being an American sailor," said Scuttlebutt. "Why even old Preacher Meadows off the *Iwo Jima* got fined and everybody knows Preacher never took a drink in his life and has a good conduct medal for every one of his four hitches."

"It's funny," said Fatso, "some of these Frenchmen aren't bad Joes. They treat you pretty good—at least as long as you got dough in your pocket—and I don't think they like the gendarmes any more than we do. If we could get them stirred up enough maybe . . ."

At this point Satchelaft entered and was hailed by all hands. "You were terrific tonight, Grandmaw," said Scuttlebutt. "When you retire you're a cinch for a job as Mother Superior of the Little Sisters of the Poor."

Satchelaft barked his shins on a bucket adrift near the door and cut loose a blast of seagoing language that cast serious doubt on this last statement. When he calmed down Fatso continued, "Y'know, Scuttlebutt, I been thinking—"

"Oh-oh," said Satchelaft. "Here we go again." All hands knew that whenever Fatso started thinking, strange things often happened to somebody. They all edged in closer and listened eagerly.

Now, Hear This!

"You speak French pretty good, don't you Satchelaft?" asked Fatso.

"Like a native," replied Satchelaft. "My mother was a 1917 war bride from Paris."

"Okay—that's fine. Scuttlebutt, you know how we always have trouble with the cops in Nice and—"

"You're telling me! When we were there for the 4th of July, I had three of them beat up fair and square the last night until that fourth guy clobbered me from behind."

"Well, we gotta find a way to stop that kind of stuff and bust up their racket," said Fatso.

"That's easy," replied Scuttlebutt, who was a man of action rather than words. "All we gotta do is get about 500 sailors, march up to the hoosegow, and tear the joint down."

"No-o-o," said Fatso. "That ain't subtle enough. We might be criticized by people who don't understand us. We got to work on public opinion and get the citizens on our side . . ."

"Sure. Just give them all a sack full of dollars and we'd have the job made. But there's a lot of Frenchmen in Nice and we haven't got enough sacks."

"Maybe there's another way of doing it," said Fatso. "Instead of making them like *us*, we can get them mad at the cops. Nobody cares how much the cops kick sailors around but I'll bet they'd get awful mad if the gendarmes pulled the same stuff on the local citizens."

"Sure they would, but these French cops are too smart to do that."

"I know," said Fatso. "But we can booby-trap them and make the people *think* they are doing it."

"Okay Fatso, we're listening," said several voices.

"They're having the big Mardi Gras parade while we are in there this time. Everybody in town turns out to see it and the Mayor and all the big wheels will be in the reviewing stand. If we could fix it so something happens in front of the reviewing stand and everybody thinks the cops are picking on some perfectly harmless local character, maybe we could do ourselves some good, or at least do the cops some harm, and that's the same thing."

"Uh-huh," said Scuttlebutt. "What kind of opium are you smoking these days, Fatso?"

"This ain't as crazy as it sounds," said Fatso. "At the Mardi Gras back home in New Orleans last year the cops tried to arrest a guy who was stealing a car. A crowd of half-jingled citizens thought they were pinning a bum rap on the guy and a hell of a rhubarb got started."

"Sure, we all heard about that in the papers," said Scuttlebutt. "But Frenchmen are different from Americans."

"Okay, so they're different," said Fatso. "We won't get any *big* rhubarb started. We'll just make them mad at the cops, stir up public opinion, and maybe get the Mayor to put the blast on his police."

"I'm in favor of it—but how are you gonna *do* it?" asked Beer Bottle.

"By strategy," replied Fatso. "Suppose Satchelaft here dresses up in his grandma costume. He makes the most official-looking old lady I've ever seen, and besides, he's got a score to settle with these cops. If he gets into an argument with the gendarmes right in front of the reviewing stand . . ."

"Maybe you got something there," said Satchelaft. "I could just walk up to the Chief of Police and bust him one in the nose."

"That's no good," said Fatso. "You're supposed to be a nice little old lady who wouldn't be mean to a mouse. You can't go round clobbering cops. We want them to push *you* around."

"It won't work," said Beer Bottle. "Satch looks too harmless. Why when he puts on that grandma costume and goes tottering around, even Commissar Jones would take time out to help him across the street. No cop would raise a hand to him no matter what he did."

"So we pull more strategy on them," said Fatso. "We supply our own cop—a phony. We can hire a gendarme outfit from a costume shop during the Mardi Gras. We take some great big bruiser like Scuttlebutt, dress him up as a cop, and let him clobber grandma real good, right out where everybody sees it!"

This was hailed as a stroke of genius by all hands except Scuttlebutt. "Yeah," he said dubiously, "it sounds great, except I'd wind up doing a twenty-year hitch in the Foreign Legion. If we pulled that in New Orleans I'd be lynched."

"If we work it right," said Fatso, "nothing will happen to you at all. The real cops will look the other way and will keep away from you and grandma as if you was poison. You can haul grandma down the street a few blocks toward the clink and then the two of you take a powder and beat it back to the ship."

By now the possibilities of Fatso's scheme were beginning to sink in. For the next couple of hours the meeting in the incinerator room resembled a conference in the Admiral's cabin when the staff is planning a major naval operation. An estimate of the situation was drawn up, carefully balancing the pros and cons of various possible courses of action. The Joint Chiefs of Staff would have been proud of the logical, systematic way this was done, applying the principles of war and weighing the advantages of surprise and the initiative. Years of experience at sea gives a group such as Fatso's an instinctive insight into sound tactical procedure—particularly for a mission designed to produce a rhubarb with the cops.

When the last detail had been worked out, Fatso said, "This is one of those things where most anything can happen, but we've got nothing to lose even if the whole thing flops. Suppose it falls flat on its face and a bunch of us wind up in the clink? So we get fined an armful of francs, but that's what always happens anyway even when we don't do nothing."

"What was it you said one time," asked Beer Bottle, "that the

Admirals call it when they get a wild idea that they're not sure is any good, but they just go ahead and have a shot at it anyway?"

"A calculated risk," said Fatso. "And that's exactly what this is."

Two days later the *Okinawa* stood in to the harbor of Nice with all the usual pomp and circumstance that accompanies the arrival of a flagship in a foreign port. The crew lined up on the flight deck in their dress blue uniforms, with the Marine guard and band stationed up forward ready to render appropriate honors, and the saluting guns' crews stood by their stations with enough ammunition broken out to re-enact the battle of Manila Bay. As the entrance buoy came abeam and the ship slowed to one-third speed, the Officer of the Deck saluted the Captain and said:

"Permission to fire a twenty-one-gun national salute, Sir?"

"Fire away," said the Skipper. "KABLAM" went the starboard gun. As the tricolor fluttered out from the main truck, the Chief Gunner went into the traditional gunner's ritual for spacing his shots five seconds apart. "If I wasn't a gunner I wouldn't be here, ready, two . . . FIRE!" "KABOOM" went the port gun . . . "away from my home and wife so dear, ready, three . . . FIRE!" "KABLAM" went the starboard gun . . . and so on for twenty-one good solid KABLAMS and KABOOMS. On the last KABLAM the French signal station ran up the Stars and Stripes at the yardarm and the shore battery blasted away in the same cadence, returning the salute gun for gun as per time-honored international custom.

A few minutes later, as the *Okinawa* coasted up to her assigned berth, the great bower anchor plunged to the bottom and the chain rattled out, touching off another exchange of KABLAMS and KABOOMS as the senior British, French, and Italian men-of-war already in port paid their respects to the American Admiral and he acknowledged them. These were personal salutes, answered gun for gun if fired by a foreign navy, but only in proportion to the saluter's rank if by our own. The young OOD has to have his wits about him and his thumb in the Reg Book at the right place while this is going on. One KABOOM too many or too few will get him ten days in his room.

While the harbor was re-echoing from the exchange of courtesies with the ships still wreathed in smoke, the Quartermaster on watch at the starboard gangway squinted through a long glass at a smart-looking launch headed for the *Okinawa* and sang out, "Official caller . . . four side boys . . . full guard and band." The OOD yanked the switch to the boat gongs in the cabin country twice, summoning the Captain and Chief of Staff to meet the visitor. As he was instructing the bugler to call away the full guard and band, the Quartermaster yelled, "Belay that last word, Sir! It's only the Mayor—four boys, guard of the day, and *no* band . . . I mistook his flag for a Prefect General," he added apologetically.

The Captain and Chief of Staff came clattering down the ladder to the quarterdeck just as the Mayor's launch was approaching the gangway. Two side boys were already stationed on each side of the upper gangway platform and a squad of Marines was standing by to present arms. As the visitor stepped out of the boat, the bosun's mate of the watch started a prolonged blast on his pipe which had to last until hizzoner arrived on deck. This was no mean feat, because an aircraft carrier's gangway is long and steep, and French Mayors are short and fat. Any bosun's mate will tell you it takes a good man to pipe a Mayor aboard. Hizzoner and the bosun's mate both just barely lasted to the top of the gangway.

The Chief of Staff led the way up several more ladders to the cabin, where the Admiral greeted them. Hizzoner bowed deeply to the Admiral, pumped his outstretched hand up and down once and stated, "I am pleasure by welcome for you, your great ships and your brave men coming to Nice and the Riviera." The Admiral motioned for all hands to be seated and made the customary witticism about the American Navy only being able to offer them coffee. Everyone laughed dutifully and said that was just what they wanted anyway. After the polite inquiries about the health of the Presidents of France and the United States, the Mayor invited the Admiral, Captain and Chief of Staff to be his guests in the reviewing stand at the Mardi Gras parade, and to assist him in judging the floats. The Admiral accepted graciously and then steered the parley into more serious channels.

"Monsieur le maire," he said, "I have a request to make of you."

"But of course," said hizzoner. "Your command is my wish."

"My sailors," said the Admiral, "sometimes have trouble with your police and . . ."

"Ah, eet ees nozzings," said the Mayor tolerantly. "We know how sailors are. We do not mind when they become a little gay."

"I know *you* understand," said the Admiral. "But sometimes your police arrest my men unjustly."

"I am desolated," said hizzoner.

"And they fine them many francs," continued the Admiral.

This was news to the Mayor, who was supposed to get a cut of all the routine fines levied in police court. "This must be mistakes," said the Mayor. "The police ledgers do not show any francs collected from your sailors."

"That's just what I thought," said the Admiral. "But when the *Salem* was in here last week, her sailors paid over a million francs in fines to the police."

A hard glint came into the Mayor's eye. "A million francs?" he said. "I make investigations right away. It is a scandal."

Then obviously distressed by this turn of the conversation and to wind things up on an even keel he said, "Admiral, to prove the friendship of France for your great Navy, I also invite your sailors for guests at ze Mardi Gras parade. We will reserve special place of honor in front of reviewing stand. 'Ow many men will you bring?"

"That's very kind of you indeed," said the Admiral. "I think

213

about 1,000 will be enough."

"We reserve special place for 1,000," said the Mayor. "And now, mon Admiral, I must go. I await your coming kindly."

Hizzoner went straight back to the city hall, yanked the Prefect of Police up on the carpet, demanded an accounting of the fines levied on the *Salem*'s sailors, and put the blast on him and his gendarmes for their treatment of American sailors, and for failing to give him his cut on their fines.

The Mardi Gras at Nice is quite a whingding. The Riviera is always a carefree place where most anything goes, but throughout the year the whoop-de-doo is usually confined to the visiting tourists. At Mardi Gras time the local citizens get into the act. They dress up in wondrous costumes, get comfortably swacked on one side, and don't have an enemy in the world. The gendarmes are especially tolerant at this time because, naturally, when the whole town goes on a binge, they have to be.

The big event of Mardi Gras is the parade on Shrove Tuesday. Everybody turns out for this and thousands jam the waterfront boulevard for miles along the route and pack the sides of the Plaza where the reviewing stand is set up. Here the Mayor and all the civic dignitaries review the parade, judge the floats, and award the coveted prizes for the best ones. The square is packed hours before the parade begins by happy citizens, filled with liberty, equality, fraternity, and cognac. Thrifty Frenchmen who wouldn't give you the correct time free on any other day relax and get friendly on this one.

On Mardi Gras Day Fatso and his cohorts were ashore bright and early. At the Last Chance Bar and Grill, Satchelaft shifted into his grandma costume and Scuttlebutt donned his gendarme outfit rented from the local costumery. It closely resembled the real thing but was just enough different in detail to beat any possible rap for impersonating an officer.

As "grandma" made her way to the Plaza, accompanied by six

husky sailors who helped her across streets and made way for her through the crowds, everyone beamed at the little old lady and her sailor friends. They were met at the Plaza by "gendarme" Scuttlebutt, who escorted them through the happy throng to a place in the sailors' special reserved section right in front of the reviewing stand, and then took station himself about ten feet out in the square in front of them. All around the square about every fifty feet were real gendarmes standing at ease, their backs to the crowd and their hands clasped behind them.

While waiting for the Mayor's party to arrive, Fatso, like any good military commander, gave his troops a final rundown on the Op-Order. "We'll stick to our plan," he said, "except for one or two little things we may have to play by ear to get the timing just right. Remember that Satchelaft and Scuttlebutt do all the real dirty work with just a little help from the rest of us. If they do things right these cops will be mighty unpopular by the time the parade is over." Then, after casing the set-up carefully, he said, "Those gendarmes on each side of Satchelaft are a little too close. We've got to get them out of the way. Beer Bottle, that's your job—a little later."

Five minutes before the parade was to begin, the Mayor's party, including the Admiral and Captain, took their places in the stands and Fatso gave the signal for Operation "Little Rhubarb" to begin. Beer Bottle eased along in front of the crowd till directly behind one of the cops to be taken out of the play and then walked unsteadily out into the square as if intending to cut directly across it. The gendarme hailed him to come back and when Beer Bottle continued on his somewhat zigzag way, the cop took off after him, got him by the arm and started leading him back to the sidelines. The route back took them past the second gendarme marked for removal from the scene and as they passed him, Beer Bottle jerked his arm loose and broke for the other side of the square again. He was soon overhauled by the two gendarmes and led out of the square waving gaily at the crowd which hooted, whistled, and booed at the gendarmes. This diversion served two purposes in the general plan: it got rid of two cops who were strategically placed to louse things up, and it focused the attention of the crowd on the gendarmes, preparing the citizens for the bigger and better things to come.

Before making his next move, Fatso waited till the blaring of martial music announced that the head of the parade was only a block away. If things went according to plan, this left just time enough for Scuttlebutt and Satchelaft to do their stuff, get out of the way, and leave the people with something to talk about after the parade was over.

At a sign from Fatso, Satchelaft took off.

The thousands packed around the square and in the reviewing stand saw a frail, bent-over, kindly old lady carrying a large net market bag, totter out into the square past Scuttlebutt. The "gendarme" apparently didn't notice her until she was twenty feet or so past him, at which point he hailed her to come back. The poor little old lady was obviously hard of hearing because she kept right on, so Scuttlebutt strode after her yelling things in French that were not very polite and that immediately focused the attention of the crowd on the little old lady. Catching up with her, he seized her rudely by the arm and spun her around, bringing a gasp out of the crowd. The other cops, seeing that one of their number was handling the situation, however crudely, and was obviously plenty big enough and in need of no assistance, remained at their posts and looked the other way. Scuttlebutt bent over till his face was only a few inches from the Old Lady's, gesticulated in a blustering manner, and pointed emphatically back in the direction from which she had come. The little old lady appeared to be completely bewildered and paralyzed with fright. She cringed away from the towering cop, clasped her hands in a pleading gesture, and bowed her head as if in prayer. Scuttle-

216

butt grabbed her by the arm, yanked her roughly toward the sidelines, and she dropped her market bag, spilling apples all over the pavement and liberating two chickens which took off erratically in opposite directions cackling in panic. By now the blaring band indicated the parade was only half a block away, but everyone was watching the little drama being enacted out in the square and angry mutters were rising from the crowd.

"Okay, boys," said Fatso to his eager helpers. "You guys get out there now, pick up the apples for her, and we've got this job made." Out dashed four sailors and began picking up the apples. As the crowd cheered this gallant gesture, Scuttlebutt scooped the little old lady up in his arms and began carrying her back to the sidelines.

Up to this point everything had gone according to plan, the act had followed the script, and things were turning out exactly as per calculations. But as so often happens on these calculated risk operations, Lady Luck took a hand at this point and upset the applecart. The cops were definitely in bad odor now and the American sailors were tops, but Satchelaft and Scuttlebutt, carried away by success, overplayed their parts.

The Little Old Lady, being lugged away by Scuttlebutt like a sack of potatoes, suddenly came to life, started kicking her heels, threw her arms up in the air and in doing so knocked the "gendarme's" hat off. Scuttlebutt dropped her abruptly on the hard pavement, picked up his hat, and then hauled off and booted the prostrate grandmother smack in the stern sheets.

This was carrying things too far—even in France. An outraged roar went up from the crowd and a dozen angry citizens broke from the sidelines to rescue the old lady. As Fatso's cohorts dropped the apples and also rushed to her assistance, Scuttlebutt hauled out his club and flailed away at all comers. The club was a harmless phony of cork, but each sailor that he clobbered with it promptly dropped like a stunned ox, and soon three apparently unconscious sailors were stretched out on the pavement. Scuttle-butt grabbed the old lady by the scruff of the neck, jerked her to her feet, and began dragging her off again.

At this point Fatso lost control of operations, and from here on it was like a flash fire followed by an explosion. The head of the parade was just entering the square, but citizens, cops and sailors swarmed out into the plaza to save grandma from the brutal gendarme. The real gendarmes converged on Scuttlebutt with the same intentions as all the other citizens—to rescue the old lady—but the citizens didn't think so. Yelling with rage, they all turned on the nearest gendarme, and the cops, in self-defense, began swinging back. In a few seconds the biggest battle since the inva-sion of France was underway. Frenchmen fought that day as they hadn't fought since the war of 1870, and the gendarmes, out-numbered 100 to 1, took the worst beating that they had since the Nazi storm troopers came to town.

The rioting spread both ways from the square like a chain reaction, engulfing the head of the parade just entering the plaza. The momentum of the parade piled the following floats up on the leaders, and soon pandemonium reigned supreme. Citizens who had no idea what was happening in the square slugged each other and the cops, demolished the leading floats, and runaway horses charged back through the parade, scattering merrymakers like tenpins.

By the time the storm blew itself out, several hundred assorted citizens, sailors, and paraders had been hauled off to the clink by the battered and indignant cops, the plaza and boulevard were littered with the wreckage of floats, and all chance of holding the parade had gone down the drain. In the wild fracas Satchelaft and Scuttlebutt managed to shed their costumes, fade into the crowd, and by the time calm was restored again, had caught a boat back to the *Okinawa*. On the way out to the ship, Satchelaft said in an awed voice, "Migawd, this is awful. We'll all get general courts—

218

it might even cause war between the United States and France."

"Yeah," said Scuttlebutt, "I don't doubt it."

Peace had hardly reared its bruised and bloody head again along the waterfront when the Mayor stormed into the police station like an angry whirlwind. He fired the Prefect of Police forthwith, busted the Chief down to gendarme apprentice and ordered all prisoners released immediately. He only meant the ones picked up in the big rhubarb, but the terrified cops took him literally and emptied the jail clean, releasing numerous pickpockets, pimps, prostitutes, and a score of assorted malefactors and vagrants.

Next morning hizzoner the Mayor came out to the *Okinawa* to call on the Admiral again. Wire services had picked up the news of the riot and flashed it around the world, and the Mayor came to offer his abject apologies. "If I hadn't seen it with my own veritable eyes, I never would believe it," he said sadly.

The Admiral took a broad view of the matter and assured the Mayor that there were no hard feelings.

Hizzoner hauled a copy of the local bladder from his pocket and pointed to a blistering editorial denouncing the police and praising American sailors to the skies. "This is the sentiment of the people," he said. "France is eternally grateful to her brave American liberators." Hizzoner then took his departure and upon arrival ashore headed immediately for the police station to collect his cut on those fines from the *Salem*, knowing full well that there would be no more for a long time.

Immediately after seeing the Mayor off, the Captain repaired to the Admiral's cabin. "What's the dope, Sir? Is he wise?" asked the Captain anxiously.

"He hasn't got the foggiest idea what really happened," said the Admiral, grinning from ear to ear. "He fell for it just like I did, until you recognized that old lady sailor of yours, just before the crowd exploded."

"So-o-o-?" asked the Captain, "What—uh—do we do now, Sir?

Now, Hear This!

Can we—er—sweep it under the rug?"

"What else could we do with it?" demanded the Admiral. "I'd have a hell of a time trying to explain it to the Mayor or the Chief of Naval Operations now. And anyway, I'll bet that gendarme who started the whole thing still thinks she *was* an old lady. Matter of fact, the way it turned out, it will do more to cement friendly relations with the French than anything since General Pershing made his speech about 'Lafayette, we are here'—and besides, it would look very unseamanlike to hang an old lady from the yard-arm of my flagship."

That night after taps Fatso and his crew met as usual in the incinerator. All hands sported black eyes, bruised knuckles, patched faces, and broad grins. "Alky" Hall, the Marine orderly who was on watch outside the Admiral's cabin that morning (with his ear glued to the keyhole) rendered a highly colored report of the Admiral's interviews with the Mayor and the Captain.

"Whaddeya know," said Beer Bottle, after hearing "Alky's" tale. "Those two old buzzards were wise to the whole thing!"

"No they weren't," corrected Scuttlebutt. "They still think I was a real gendarme."

"Just goes to show how natural you look being ornery and mean," said Satchelaft, who still couldn't sit down comfortably.

"It's like I told you guys about a calculated risk," said Fatso smugly. "If you're real smart, figure all the angles out ahead of time, and allow for everything that may happen, it's the same as money in the bank."

⚓ CHAPTER TWELVE

The Disappearing Periscope

THE SIXTH FLEET, fresh from a ten-day visit to Naples, knifed through the Mediterranean in cruising formation—two dozen ships maneuvering like Navy's Sugar Bowl team, with an umbrella of fifty planes droning overhead. In the quarterback's spot at the center of the formation the *Okinawa*, acting fleet flagship, called the signals and ran the show. Huddled around her on Circle 2 were four heavy cruisers; way out on Circle 20 a squadron of destroyers formed a circular antisubmarine screen, protecting the heavy ships against torpedo attack. The fleet was preparing for a scheduled exercise against a group of British submarines from Malta. Today they were to limber up by repelling mock attacks by one of our own subs.

"P-i-i-ing" went the sonar head that stuck out under the keel of the destroyer *Dillberry*, stationed in the formation's outer screen. In the sound room just above the keel, surrounded by a Buck Rogers array of electronic gear, dials, switches, computers, and indicators, all hands on watch looked half asleep, as sonar crews always do when they have been pinging away for hours with nothing happening.

Now, Hear This!

The chief in charge nodded over a whodunit, while two control plotters rolled a leisurely game of acey-deucey with the attack-director operator idly kibitzing. Only the sonarman on watch at the set paid any outward attention to what was going on. He sat there with his phones clamped to his head, watching the video scope, while the constant "Ping . . . ping . . . ping" hammered into his brain.

The operating principle of a sonar set is very simple. The sound head lets out a "P-i-i-ing" into the water and, after allowing enough time for an echo to come back—if it's going to—it swings over a few degrees and makes another "ping." All day long this goes on, "ping . . . ping . . . ping," while the sound head swings its probing beam from port to starboard and vice versa, searching for an echo to indicate there is something out there besides salt water of uniform temperature, density, and emptiness. No wonder sonar operators soon become "ping-happy" characters for whom their shipmates make tolerant allowances.

Suddenly the *Dillberry*'s operator sat up and began fiddling with the knobs on his set. He thought maybe he had heard something. After the next "Ping," he flipped the switch cutting his set in on the sound room's loudspeaker. He was pretty sure he was hearing something. All hands looked up from their extracurricular business in mild curiosity as the loudspeaker repeated the outgoing "p-i-i-ing"—and then leaped to their stations as a faint but unmistakable "pong" came back.

"I got an echo, bearing zero-four-five, three thousand yards, sir," reported the operator over the bridge phone. As the plotters grabbed pencils and bent over their chart boards, the chief buckled on his battle phone and the attack-director operator began cranking dials on the mechanical brain of the ship.

After the next faint "pong" the sonarman reported, "Bearing zero-four-five, two nine eight zero yards. Good solid echo, sir." The plotters made new marks on their charts and the director

222

The Disappearing Periscope

operator prompted his robot brain with more data to help it solve the course and speed of whatever it was that the sonarman was pinging on.

By now the chief was peering at the scope over the sonarman's shoulder.

"Whatcha got, son?" he muttered. "A school of fish?"

"Not this time, chief," said the operator. "This is too solid"— and a good crisp "pong" came back to confirm his diagnosis. "Contact evaluated as possible submarine," he reported to the bridge; "Zero-four-four, two thousand nine hundred and fifty yards."

The next "ping" and the first stroke of the general alarm rang out simultaneously, as squawk boxes all over the ship blared the words: "Man your battle stations! Submarine contact!"

On the bridge, the skipper came scrambling out of his sea cabin, sizing up the situation as he took station behind the helmsman. "Steady as you go, son," he said. "Hold her right on course."

One "pong" out of the loudspeaker told the skipper's experienced ear that this wasn't a school of fish or a thermal layer. "Sounds like a sub all right," he said. "Helmsman, shift to sonar now. Follow the course-order indicator."

"Aye, aye, sir," said the helmsman, flipping his controller to give her a touch of rudder and swing her left to match pointers with the indicator from the sonar room.

Up ahead, planes swooped down, laying a sonobuoy pattern, dropping cylindrical floats about the size of golf bags that floated end-up in the water, stuck up a whip antenna, and broadcast by radio the sounds they picked up from underwater microphones.

"The planes must think there's something there too," observed the skipper.

Down in the sonar room, where a dozen men were now jamming into their battle stations, the "pongs" were following the "pi-i-ings" more quickly and getting louder as the range decreased.

223

Now, Hear This!

The sub, obviously aware that she had been detected, swerved radically and went deep to evade attack. But the probing sonar beam stayed on it, feeding the dope into the attack director, which kept generating the proper course to counter each evasive maneuver and transmitting it to the indicator on the bridge:

"P-i-i-ing . . . pong . . . p-i-i-ing . . . pong . . . p-i-i-ing . . . pong," went the sonar, increasing in tempo and volume as the firing point came closer.

"Stand by for full depth-charge pattern!" barked the control officer into the battle-circuit squawk box. Back on the fantail at the racks and Y guns, sailors went through the motions of readying depth charges and projectors for an attack.

In the sonar room, machines and electronic tubes were doing the thinking now, while men performed purely mechanical functions for them. A dozen eyes were glued on the big dial of the attack director, where a moving white arrow representing the destroyer converged relentlessly on the squirming submarine arrow. The control officer nudged the sailor alongside him as the arrows were about to meet.

"Stand by-y-y-y!" he sang out. "Fire!!"

The sailor squeezed his firing key, the attack director lit up with red lights like a Christmas tree, and there was a rippling series of pops back on the fantail as miniature projectors flung a salvo of small noise bombs into the air, simulating full-size depth charges.

The bombs arched out and hit the water in the same pattern as depth charges would. As they sank to proper depth and exploded, the people on the target sub, with their sensitive listening gear, knew instantly whether this attack, had it been the McCoy, would have merely jarred the fillings out of their teeth or would have split them wide open and sent them to Davy Jones.

Up on the bridge, the helmsman put on full right rudder to circle for another attack. Soon the jubilant word came up from the sonar room, "Sub's underwater phone reports we made two direct

The Disappearing Periscope

hits! She says she is surfacing."

Seconds later, a lookout yelled, "Periscope two hundred yards on starboard quarter!"

All glasses on the bridge swung over to the bearing, and sure enough, there it was! No fish or other phonies this time!

The attack periscope of a submarine close aboard is an evil-looking thing that makes your skin crawl even in peacetime. It is unmistakable, although thousands of false periscopes are sighted all over the ocean in wartime by people who don't know what a periscope looks like. But once you have really seen one, you never forget.

The visible part tapers and is about the size and shape of a slim-handled baseball bat, with a distinctive hood over the prism at the handle end. It sticks straight up out of the water three or four feet and throws up spray as it moves along. No ocean rubbish really resembles it, not even a swab floating with its handle sticking up.

"Yep," said the skipper, as his glasses picked up the periscope. "That's it all right. He's casing the setup before he surfaces all the way."

Soon a huge black shape heaved itself up from the depths, white water pouring off its sides. Planes dived down and snarled around the sub like dogs harrying a wounded bear, the hatch popped open and the skipper climbed out on the conning tower. Facing the *Dillberry*, he clasped both hands over his head and shook them in the traditional gesture, indicating to the "can" that she had done a good job.

That night, down in the incinerator compartment of the *Okinawa*, Fatso and his cronies gathered for their usual evening meeting.

"That tin can sure clobbered the submarine today," observed Satchelaft between mouthfuls.

"Yeah," said Fatso, "this new destroyer squadron we just got from the States looked pretty good on that drill."

All the group nodded judicial agreement.

"I was hoping the sub would make bums out of them," said Satchelaft.

"How come, Satchelaft?" demanded Fatso. "Why do you talk like that?"

"I don't like this new squadron commander that came over with them from the States. I had trouble with him ashore in Naples."

"My, my!" said Fatso. "You shouldn't go round having trouble on liberty with four-stripe captains in foreign ports. Wha' hoppen?"

"The last night we were in Naples," said Satchelaft, "I was on the dock waiting for the midnight boat . . ."

"Minding your own business, saying nothing to nobody," interrupted Fatso, "when this four-stripe captain comes along and picks a fight with you? We've heard that one before. You've got to do better than that."

"Don't butt in, wise guy," said Satchelaft. "I just happened to be on the dock when the four-striper fell overboard, and he seems to blame me for it."

"How come?"

"There was a little misunderstanding up in town that night at the Black Cat Bar, but nothing was really out of line till the bartender went and called the cops. Then some crazy destroyer sailor heaved a gendarme out the window on the second floor. That got the other cops excited, so I got out of there. Tables, chairs, and empty bottles were flying around pretty thick, and in the confusion I lost my white hat and wound up wearing one of the cops' hats—you know those funny black three-cornered hats like John Paul Jones wore? Well I was still wearing it down on the dock, waiting for the boat. I guess it must of made me kind of conspicuous, because this four-striper comes along to wait for his boat, and tells me I'm on the report for being out of uniform!"

226

The Disappearing Periscope

"I doubt if our Old Man will give you anything worse than a warning for that," said Fatso. "What are you so worried about?"

"You ain't heard the half of it yet. He took this hat away from me, and while we were standing there on the dock and I was trying to explain about it, a wild-eyed Eyetalian cop without a hat comes barreling down the ramp, rushes up to the four-striper and snatches the hat out of his hands. The cop was pretty excited, and I think he figured it was the four-striper who swiped his hat, because he put the blast on him in Eyetalian, jumping up and down and waving his arms."

"Boy, I'd like to have seen that," said Scuttlebutt appreciatively.

"But that ain't all. The skipper was standing near the edge of the dock, with his back to the water, and this crazy Eyetalian was crowding him, so he went to push the cop back a little, and the cop hauled off and shoved him smack overboard! He was the maddest four-striper I've ever seen when I dragged him back on the float. By that time the gendarme had beat it and this four-striper blamed me for the whole thing."

"Well, now, after all," said Fatso, "I don't see where you got too much to worry about. Our Old Man is pretty broad-minded about routine mixups like that."

"But this guy said he wasn't going to make no routine report to the skipper about it. He said he would take it up personally with the Admiral next time he saw him."

"Oh-oh," said Fatso. "That's bad. Things sometimes get exaggerated when that happens."

"Yeah," said Scuttlebutt. "And by the time it gets to the Old Man there is so much heat on that he's got to do something drastic."

"We're going to be out here on this submarine exercise with the British for the next week," said Fatso, "so he won't see the Admiral till we get in to Algiers."

Now, Hear This!

"But as soon as he does, I'll be restricted," said Satchelaft, "and I won't even get ashore to see little Marie in Algiers. Some tin-can sailor will probably beat my time with her," he added bitterly.

"Who is this new four-striper, anyway?" demanded Beer Bottle.

"He's a fat little guy by the name of Smoak," said Scuttlebutt. "He's an old-time destroyer man."

"Not 'G.S.' Smoak?" asked Fatso with interest.

"Yeah, that's it—G.S. Smoak. I seen his name on the operation plan for the destroyers' antisub exercise," said Scuttlebutt.

"Well, blow me down," said Fatso. "Old 'Gumshoe' Smoak. But don't ever call him that to his face. I know him from way back."

"Can you fix it with him?" asked Satchelaft eagerly.

"Not a chance, bub," said Fatso. "That guy has been on the make for admiral ever since I can remember. He's always ear-banging with his seniors. He's a classmate of our Old Man, so they will come up for selection to admiral at the same time, and there's nothing he'd rather do than come running to the Admiral with a story about how our Old Man's undisciplined sailors are raising hell ashore."

"Looks like I'm just a small piece of stuff in a high-level meat-grinder," said Satchelaft.

"Whaddeya know?" said Fatso reminiscently. "My old pal, Gumshoe Smoak! He got me busted from chief on the hitch before last. It was a bum rap too! You shouldn't of hauled him back out of the water, Satchelaft."

"Next time I won't."

"Let's think about this thing," said Fatso, getting that faraway look in his eye that all the gang knew from experience meant, "Caution! Man at work."

"Wouldn't it be nice," said Fatso after a pause, "if this new destroyer squadron fell flat on its face in this submarine exercise with the British? Then old Gumshoe would be so busy alibiing for

228

it when we got in to Algiers that he probably wouldn't have time to tell the Admiral any funny stories about sailors he met on the dock in Naples."

"Yeah," said Satchelaft. "And it would be nice, too, if we all got promoted to chief. But this bunch of cans isn't going to fall flat on its face. You saw how they clobbered our own sub today."

"I know," said Fatso, "but I've had a little stunt in the back of my mind that I've wanted to try for years. This might be a good time for it."

"What is it, Fatso?" asked several eager voices.

"Suppose," said Fatso, "that on this big submarine exercise, every time the destroyers got a sound contact, we had a periscope pop up just a couple of hundred yards astern of us about ten minutes later. That would make bums out of the cans, wouldn't it?"

There were eager nods all around the circle. "But how can we make that happen, Fatso?" asked Scuttlebutt. Knowing Fatso, as they all did, this query was simply a request for enlightenment, rather than any expression of doubt.

"Suppose we had some floating models of the upper end of an attack periscope that we could drop overboard at just the right time, and suppose we have the right guys on lookout watch, and they're tipped off so they'll spot them, give the alarm and make sure the admiral sees them."

There was a brief pause while all hands mulled that one over cautiously, and finally Satchelaft said, "Yeah, but . . ."

"Sure, I know it isn't quite as simple as that," said Fatso. "There's a few details that have to be worked out. But we have enough talent here to do it. You can't leave these things floating back there, or the destroyers would finally fish one out of the water and spoil the deal. We've got to fix them so they'll sink after a few minutes—which is like what a sub does anyway. It doesn't keep that attack 'scope sticking up forever; it submerges. And we don't want these things to just sit there as if they were dead in the water. We've got to fix it so they throw up a little spray, like they were moving."

By now, all hands were buying Fatso's plan enthusiastically . . . all except Satchelaft, who, having the most at stake, was more cautious. "But how are we gonna do it?" he asked.

"We gotta organize the job and divide it up. "Chips," said Fatso, addressing the carpenter's mate seated on the farthest bucket, "you've got all kinds of wood-turning equipment in the carpenter shop. Can you make us half a dozen models of the upper end of a periscope? You know what it looks like, it's kind of—"

"Yeah, I know. I spent the whole war in the Atlantic and I seen hundreds of 'em," said Chips, multiplying by the factor of ten always used by seafaring men in recounting their war experiences.

"All right," continued Fatso. "Make them out of light pine, paint them dull black like a periscope, and put a small piece of glass on top for the sun to glint on."

"O.K. That's easy," said Chips.

"Now we gotta have something to make these things float straight up. Sparky," said Fatso, addressing the electronics technician, "you've got a lot of surveyed sonobuoys in your storeroom. If we put our model periscope on top of a sonobuoy, it will stick up just the way we want it to, like the whip antenna does. All you gotta do is fix those sonobuoys so they will sink after about five minutes, instead of after an hour, like they are designed for. Can you do that?"

"Sure," said Sparky eagerly, "I'll just enlarge one vent hole to about—"

"O.K.," said Fatso. "You work out the details. Now all we got left is the matter of making it throw up some spray. Who has any ideas about that?"

"No strain there," said Scuttlebutt. "We can get some of those small oxygen bottles that the aviators have on their bail-out kits.

230

The Disappearing Periscope

Lash one of them to the sonobuoy with the vent pointing up, and it will blow up a small storm for about ten minutes."

"Well, there you are, boys," said Fatso. "The exercise starts the day after tomorrow. Let's have six of these things up here by tomorrow afternoon." Having made this command decision, the meeting adjourned.

Next evening when the board of strategy met, six sonobuoys with evil-looking periscopes mounted on their tops and oxygen bottles lashed to their sides, just below the water line, were stacked in the after corner of the incinerator. As the steak and eggs sizzled, detailed plans were drawn up for the next day's operations.

Arrangements were made to have somebody in Fatso's gang on lookout watch throughout the day, assigned to the astern sector. Usually the far-reaching prestige and influence of Fatso's mob were exerted in keeping members off the watch lists; getting them put on was simple. Another man had to be on "duty" all day long, ready to heave the phony periscopes overboard at the proper time, and Fatso detailed himself for this job. It was decided to do this from the small oiling sponson back aft on the starboard quarter. This was an unfrequented spot concealed under the flight-deck overhang and used only when fueling destroyers. It had a battle phone to the bridge, so Fatso could listen in on what was happening and know when any destroyer made a sound contact. He could also tip off the lookout by a prearranged code word on the phone whenever he heaved a dummy overboard.

When the plans had been all worked out to everyone's satisfaction, Fatso remarked, "This is something I've wanted to do for a long time, just for fun. But now we can strike a blow for freedom with it."

The big antisub exercise the next day was one that none of the destroyer sailors who took part in it will ever forget. To their dying day they will all suspect that either the admiral went nuts or that the British used some new superduper secret device that

231

Now, Hear This!

baffled our sonar gear. On the other hand, the Limeys all thought that our destroyers put up a "good show," detecting and "destroying" every one of their attacking subs, and they have been puzzled ever since at the reluctance of our people to discuss that exercise.

The first "attack" came soon after sunrise. Two destroyers out on the port bow detected the incoming fully submerged sub simultaneously, and got off a perfect team attack, resulting in a prompt "kill." Five minutes after the destroyers reported, "Sub admits being sunk, is withdrawing from action," Fatso heaved his first "periscope" overboard.

Half a minute later, when the admiral was just about to send the destroyers a "well-done" signal, Satchelaft, standing lookout watch on the bridge, bellowed, "Periscope! Periscope, dead astern, two hundred yards!"

All hands on the navigation and flag bridges swung their glasses aft. There could be no doubt about it! There was a periscope in hot pursuit, throwing up a cloud of spray, with the sub in perfect position to fire an acoustic torpedo straight up the wake and blow the *Okinawa*'s stern off.

"Cancel that 'well-done' signal I just wrote!" roared the Admiral, after one look. Then, turning to his chief of staff, he remarked, "The Limeys sure made suckers out of us that time. Sent a decoy in ahead to distract everybody, and the real attack got through undetected. The Germans used to do it all the time. There he goes," said the Admiral, as the sonobuoy sank, dragging the "periscope" down with it. "If we were playing for keeps, we might follow him down soon—or at least have to get towed home."

The second attack that morning was practically a repetition of the first, with the destroyers making another prompt, workmanlike detection and kill. The admiral decided to outguess the Limeys, in case they were working the old decoy racket, by changing course of the formation ninety degrees away from the contact as soon as

The Disappearing Periscope

it was made, thus gumming up the approach of the second sub—if there was one. But again the attacker's periscope popped up three hundred yards astern, and everybody on the *Okinawa's* bridge got a good look at it. This called forth a peremptory signal from the admiral to Captain Smoak, demanding that he warn his destroyers to be more alert and not get so interested in the next sub that came along that they forgot about the possibility he might have a partner.

On the third attack the admiral reversed the course of the formation one hundred and eighty degrees, figuring that this would certainly snafu the Limeys. But apparently it didn't.

The admiral's blood pressure took an alarming jump when a signal came in from Captain Smoak after this fiasco suggesting that there was only one sub involved and that the *Okinawa* was seeing things. His chief of staff had trouble convincing the admiral that the proposed reply to this message could not be sent by flag signal, because certain four-letter words, adjectives and phrases that the admiral wished included do not appear in the official United States Navy Signal Book.

It was really laying it on a bit thick for Fatso to drop the last three "periscopes." But no power on land or sea could have stopped him from doing it. And by that time tempers were so short on the flag bridge that nobody in his right mind would think of telling the admiral that he had been bobby-trapped by phonies, even if they had known it—which nobody except Fatso's gang did.

At the end of the day's exercise a terse signal went out addressed to Captain Smoak, directing him to report on board *Okinawa* immediately upon arrival in Algiers, prepared to explain this humiliating international snafu.

The fleet arrived in Algiers a few days later, and that night there was a jubilant meeting of Fatso's gang in the incinerator compartment. "Alky" Hall, sergeant, USMC, held the boys spellbound with his first-hand account of what had transpired in the admiral's cabin when Captain Smoak came aboard that morning. Alky was the admiral's orderly and, although the interview between the admiral and the captain had been a private one, with no one else in the cabin, as is customary in the Navy when a senior lowers the boom on an errant junior, Alky's station was just outside the cabin door. This door was not nearly thick enough to confine the high points of that interview within the cabin bulkheads.

"Boy, oh, boy, it was really something!" said Alky. "I heard things today I hadn't heard said that way since I was a boot recruit. I hope I can remember some of them next time I go back to Parris Island as an instructor."

"What diddee say?" asked Satchelaft eagerly.

"He started off by saying, 'Smoak, I've seen more periscopes in my time than you have whiskey bottles, counting even the ones you drank yourself on the Asiatic Station.'"

"Boy, that was a hot one!" roared Satchelaft. "What else diddee say?"

"Let the man alone," said Fatso. "He'll tell us if you just give him a chance."

"He said, 'Commodore, I want you to get up off that fat ass of yours and whip those destroyers into shape!' He said, 'The —— Limeys are going to be laughing up their sleeves at me the rest of the time I'm in the Mediterranean.'"

"What else diddee say?" demanded Satchelaft, grinning from ear to ear.

"Then," continued Alky, "the four-striper really stuck his neck out. He had a briefcase full of papers with him—reports from his destroyers—and he claimed they proved absolutely that no subs had snuck through their screen. You should have heard the admiral tell him . . ."

What the admiral told him to do with those papers evoked roars of laughter from all hands, and boosted the Admiral's stock with everybody higher than if he had just been appointed Chief of Naval Operations.

"He chewed him out," said Alky, "like a master sergeant telling off a fresh-caught corporal. It was one of the most beautiful things I've ever listened to. I didn't think admirals even knew some of the words he used."

"Did this four-striper ever say anything about me?" asked Satchelaft.

"I thought he was starting to talk about you at one time," said Alky, "when he said something about 'dumb sailors.' But it turned out he meant the sonar operators on his own cans—and the admiral didn't hold still for that either," added Alky. "He said, 'Smoak, my dear fellow,' he said, 'I want it clearly understood that . . .'"

It was two bells in the midwatch before Alky finished relating and repeating all the juicy details.

At the end of this uneventful watch, the Officer of the Deck wrote in the ship's log book: "As before. No remarks!"

⚓ CHAPTER THIRTEEN

Monkey Business at Mers-el-Kebir

LIEUTENANT COMMANDER "Curly" Cue, U.S. Navy, eased back the throttles on his twin-jet Banshee fighter and put her into a gentle turn at twenty thousand feet. Glancing down over the port side of his sleek plane at the bright blue water of the Mediterranean, Curly could see what looked like a bunch of toy ships in circular formation trailing long white wakes behind them. Those toys were a task force of the U.S. Sixth Fleet. The biggest toy, in the center of the formation, was the *Okinawa*, acting flagship and currently the home of Curly's squadron.

Looking back over his right shoulder, Curly saw fifteen more Banshees flying in perfect echelon formation on him. That group of alert young eagles was the hottest fighter squadron in the U.S. Navy—if you asked Curly. For that matter, if you twisted his arm he would admit it was the hottest fighter outfit in the world.

Curly squeezed the radio transmitter button on his throttle and growled into the lip microphone fastened to his helmet, "Cowshed, this is Whambo with sixteen Banshees orbiting Cowshed at angels twenty, ready for landing. Over."

236

Monkey Business at Mers-el-Kebir

From the Combat Information Center deep inside the *Okinawa* the reply came back, "Whambo, this is Cowshed. Roger. Wait."

"Wait," Curly sneered to himself, impatiently cocking his turn up a little steeper. "Those feather merchants down there must think I've got a direct hookup to the Big Inch. Wait, I suppose, until we haven't even got enough gas left to take a waveoff. And that dizzy guy with the paddles would wave his own grandmother off if she came in a half a knot fast. Now if I was the admiral of this task group . . ."

One of the factors which had helped to get Lieutenant Commander Cue that nickname of Curly was beginning to make itself felt. Of course, anyone by the name of Cue was bound to be known as Curly, even if he were bald. And Curly wasn't bald. He had a big mop of brilliant red hair that had made feminine hearts do flip-flops all the way from Jacksonville to Coronado and from Quonset Point to Seattle. He also had the temper that went with it.

He was in a foul mood this morning because he had just led his troops on a wild-goose-chase that took them five hundred miles west of Gibraltar out over the Atlantic Ocean, searching vainly for the *Okinawa*'s sister ship, the *Woodrow Wilson*. The *Okinawa* had been in the Mediterranean for eight months, and the *Wilson* was currently en route from Norfolk to relieve her.

In a few days the two great ships would meet in the harbor of Oran, Algiers, on the Barbary Coast of Africa. There the admiral on the *Wilson* would take over command of the Mediterranean Fleet, and the *Okinawa* would hoist the homeward-bound pennant and be on her way to Norfolk. Curly's host of feminine admirers in the United States would soon be in a flat spin again.

Meantime, Admiral Day on the *Okinawa*, otherwise known as Windy, had determined to give his naval academy classmate, Admiral "Bugler" Bell on the *Wilson*, a proper reception when he arrived in European waters. Windy's nickname was a fairly accurate characterization of the man. "Bugler" had acquired his because he was such a stickler for military etiquette, and always kept a bugler handy to sound Attention, or whatever other call might be required.

These two had been friendly rivals throughout their naval careers, so Curly's admiral had sent him and his squadron out beyond Gibraltar to find the eastbound *Wilson*, welcome her to the Mediterranean, and, if possible, to surprise her with all her planes on deck and give her a thorough mock strafing. The admiral could always claim such a maneuver was part of his training program.

Curly and his covey of intrepid birdmen also had many contemporaries on the *Wilson*, so they entered into the spirit of the game gleefully. But on this current sortie they had found nothing but the Atlantic Ocean.

After circling for a few minutes, Curly noticed that the wakes of the ships in the task group were curving into the wind. Presently the voice from CIC said, "Whambo, this is Cowshed, we are turning into the wind. Your squadron is number one to land. Over."

"This is Whambo. Wilco. Out," Curly said, passing the breakup signal back along the echelon, and throttling carefully down to the minimum power at which you can idle one of those hot-air mills without the danger of blowing your fire out. Then, popping his dive brakes open and rolling gently away from the echelon, he pointed the nose of his Banshee almost straight down.

Even at idling power and with dive brakes lousing up the streamlining, it doesn't take long for a Banshee to come down twenty thousand feet. As the altimeter spun around in one direction, the airspeed meter wound itself up in the other. Before the *Okinawa* had completed her turn into the wind, Curly whooshed past the starboard side of the island close aboard.

Hauling up ahead and losing speed as he went, Curly dropped his landing gear, checking to see that it was all down and locked.

Continuing down the landing checkoff list, he dropped his hook, squirmed out of his chute, checked his shoulder harness, lowered his flaps, and banked into a standard rate turn to the left.

He gauged his turn with a practiced eye and straightened out in the groove, getting the cut signal from "Paddles" just as the white flag went up at the landing signal officer's platform, indicating "ship into wind and deck ready." As the number-two wire brought him up with a jerk, Curly shoved the hook-retriever handle and poured the coal to his jets, taxiing past the barriers at a brisk clip to clear the deck for his number-two man coming in thirty seconds behind him.

With the barriers behind him, Curly pushed the hydraulic lever to fold his wings, stuck out his fist with his thumb up as he passed flight-deck control, indicating the plane was okay for the next flight, and, following the arm and hand signals of the taxi director, eased his Banshee into a parking space between two Corsairs with six inches of elbowroom on each side. "Another day, another dollar," Curly sighed as he cut the fuel to his jets. "It all counts on thirty years."

"Lieutenant Commander Cue report to flag plot immediately," boomed the flight-deck bull horns, over the roar of powerful jets as Curly's number-three man, who had crowded number two just a mite too closely, took a wave-off and thundered past the ship to go around again.

"What ho, Curly," said Admiral Day as the squadron commander strode into flag plot. "Didn't you find them?"

"No sir," Curly said, "and we went out a good five hundred miles west of Gib."

"Yes, I know you did," Admiral Day replied. "I could hear your mob jabbering about it on the radio most of the way back. It sounded like a bunch of Air Force characters instead of a military organization. When are you going to drill some radio discipline into those jockeys of yours?"

Now, Hear This!

Curly assured the admiral that he had the names of all the offenders and intended to cut their ears off and stuff them down their throats before dinner that evening. "Uh-huh," said the Admiral. "Anyway, I'm going to send you out again tomorrow morning. The *Wilson* has an arrival time to meet in Gibraltar and so we can't help finding her tomorrow. We will make a predawn launch and you may catch old 'Bugler' still in his bunk at sunrise."

"Aye, aye, sir," Curly said with a grin.

"And incidentally," continued the admiral, handing Curly a small piece of paper, "here are the radio frequencies and call signs of the *Wilson* just in case you might have some use for them."

"Aye, aye, sir," said Curly.

A few minutes later Curly laid down the law to his pilots in the ready room. "Now I'm not going to warn you about this again. Next time there's a breach of radio discipline, I'm going to lower the boom."

"York, York, sir," croaked a barely audible voice in the rear row of seats.

Curly ignored the voice. "York, York" is the phonetic pronunciation of "YARC," which ensigns and jaygees use instead of "Aye, aye, sir" when addressing squadron commanders—behind their backs. It means "You're Absolutely Right, Commander."

"Someday," Curly continued, "one of you guys will be a couple of hundred miles away when a ship has a message for you that may mean the difference between getting back aboard and going into the drink. If you don't learn to lay off that microphone button, the ship might just as well put the message in a bottle and heave it overboard—then maybe it would wash ashore and be delivered to your beneficiaries."

"York, York, sir," croaked the voice.

"All hands turn in early tonight," Curly snapped. "Sunrise is at 0630 and we're going off at 0430."

Monkey Business at Mers-el-Kebir

As the pilots began gathering up their gear to leave, Curly added, "Oh, by the way, I've got the *Wilson's* frequencies and calls, so if you hear some yackety-yak from me on the radio to-morrow morning, that's special and doesn't count."

There were knowing grins and "York Yorks" all over the ready room.

Meantime, down in the incinerator compartment Fatso and his friends were hashing over the highlights of this Mediterranean cruise that was about to end.

"Boy oh boy," said Scuttlebutt, "two weeks from now we'll be in the good old US of A . . . But this hasn't been such a bad cruise at that. There's been a lot of things I'll never forget, like when we made them smoke screens with the incinerator, and the time we thrun all the rubbish overboard in Nice and got the *Iwo Jima* banished to Siberia."

"And, how about when we got Fatso off the hook with the Admiral," asked Beer Bottle, "by rescuing Hawsepipe from drownd-ing? That was the best one of the cruise."

"No-o-o," said Satchelaft judicially. "The best one was when we got Commissar Jones to pay 400 smackers for that dumb parrot in that cage up there."

Pete, who had been doping off on his perch, opened one eye, said "AWK" in a scornful manner and then added reminiscently, "Say something you ———— sonofabitch."

"I'm glad we're getting out of this Sixth Fleet now that this new admiral is coming," observed Fatso.

"Why? Is he a bad actor?" asked Satchelaft.

"He's a spherical S.O.B.," replied Fatso, "an S.O.B. from any angle. Bugler Bell is his name."

"Sounds like you're not very fond of him," said Beer Bottle.

"I ain't," said Fatso. "All he thinks about is spit and polish, social stuff and protocol. He was the worst ship handler I ever served with. Almost knocked the dock down every time he brought us alongside. But he can spot a suit of non-regulation blues a block away on a dark night."

"How come he made admiral?" asked Judge Jenks.

"He was a sharp operator around the Pentagon and buttered up the right guys. But everybody who served under him hated him. He busted me to second class, he did, about fifteen years ago, because I couldn't keep a straight face when a drunk distinguished visitor that I was piping aboard came staggering up the gangway, began whistling back at me, and tried to shake hands with the side boys."

"Well, he'll have plenty of protocol and stuff like that there to keep him busy after he takes over this Sixth Fleet," observed Satchelaft.

"Yeah," said Fatso. "After nearly thirty years in this here now Navy, he's one of the few guys that I'm still mad at. I'd like to square accounts with him before I retire. And I know just how to do it, too, except it's too big a deal for a flat-hat to swing by himself. I'd have to get some officer in on it too to help handle the legal matters that might crop up right afterwards."

"Hmmmmm, sounds interesting," said Beer Bottle. "Give out with it."

"No-o-o," said Fatso. "None of you guys could help. But if I could get some young officer who has a drag with our admiral to go along with me, I'd make old Bugler Bell look so foolish he'd wish he had stayed on the farm instead of going to sea."

Next morning as the sun rose over the horizon, it found the great ship *Woodrow Wilson* in a very embarrassing position. She was caught with her pants down. She was only halfway through the launching of her deck load when Curly and his squadron came boiling down and gave her a screaming welcome fore and aft and athwartships.

To add insult to injury, the *Wilson's* radio communications were soon hopelessly fouled up. When they had attempted to

Monkey Business at Mers-el-Kebir

vector their Combat Air Patrol out to intercept the attack, the CAP's orders were changed in some mysterious manner and they went off in the wrong direction. The attempt to rendezvous squadrons after take-off was characterized by orders, unauthorized counterorders, and disorder. In a short time pandemonium reigned, and all the *Wilson's* frequencies sounded like feeding time in the bird house at the zoo. Her traffic pattern went haywire, with planes swarming around in all directions.

When the *Wilson's* last plane started its take-off, Curly made a final swipe at her deck before heading east to go home. As he zoomed back up into the wild blue yonder, trouble suddenly reared its ugly head. The hand on his tail-pipe temperature gauge edged over into the red danger sector of the dial, saying to Curly, "Get on the deck in five minutes—or you will have had it."

There's only one thing you can do in a situation like that, so Curly grabbed his mike button and did it: "*Wilson, Wilson.* This is *Okinawa* One. *Mayday.* I'm coming in for emergency landing. Over."

"Mayday" is the SOS of the air, and you never use that to fool anybody. Almost immediately a disarmingly soothing voice from CIC on the *Wilson* crooned back, "Rajah! *Okinawa* One, Rajah! Come right aboard, pal. You are number one to land."

Fifteen minutes later Admiral Day on the *Okinawa* was handed the following priority message from the *Wilson:*

From: ComCarDiv FOUR
To : ComCarDiv SIX
A rough-looking character flying a crummy broken-down Banshee landed on board the *Wilson* at 0630. He speaks broken English, claims he is from *Okinawa* and that his name is Cue. Have made him a prisoner of war. Best regards, Bell.

The answer went back:

243

Now, Hear This!

From: ComCarDiv SIX
To   : ComCarDiv FOUR
Cue is dangerous and may be armed. Treat with extreme caution. Welcome to the Mediterranean. WINDY.

Just before noon that day, Curly Cue arrived back over the *Okinawa* escorted by eight Panthers from the *Wilson*. His Banshee's tail-pipe temperature was now back to normal and under control, but Curly's own temperature was clear out of sight.

As the Panther escort broke off to return to their own ship, the flight leader sang out on the radio, "Goom-by, Curly. Come see us again sometime, Goldilocks."

"You'll be sorry, you so-and-so's," was the only reply Curly could muster.

The landing signal officer had trouble getting Curly aboard that day. On his first pass up the groove, Curly came in as if he were heading for the finish line at the National Air Races. "Paddles" waved him off, turned to his helper and said, "We're going to have a bad time with Curly. It looks like his temper is in low pitch and he's got his head down and locked."

After three more passes, "Paddles" finally got him slowed down enough to give him a very dubious cut, and the Banshee pulled the number-three arresting wire clear up against the stops before coming to rest.

On the flag bridge, Admiral Day remarked, "Curly's awfully mad about something, but I don't see why he should be that mad." Then, as Curly scrambled out of the cockpit and headed for the flag bridge, the admiral said, "It might have happened to anybody."

Half a minute later, Lieutenant Commander Cue stormed into flag plot in a burst of seagoing language. The first coherent statement he was able to make was, "Those stupid clowns can't do that to me."

244

Monkey Business at Mers-el-Kebir

"Calm yourself, Curly," the admiral said. "What can't they do to you?"

"This!" roared Curly, yanking off his helmet.

For once in his naval career Admiral Day envied the handiwork of his rival, "Bugler" Bell. After a second of stunned amazement, he let out a whoop and everybody in flag plot burst into loud guffaws. Admiral Bell hadn't been fooling about that "prisoner of war" business. Curly's famous mop of red hair had been clipped down to the roots.

When decorum was finally restored in flag plot, Curly mustered a wry grin himself and said, "Okay, okay. I know I asked for it. But, Admiral, I'm going to think about this, and with your permission I may want to have a word with you later."

"By all means, Baldy, by all means," the admiral said. With that, Lieutenant Commander Cue strode out of flag plot and headed for the wardroom.

While passing through the hangar deck on the way to the wardroom, Curly encountered Fatso, who by this time, of course, knew all about the "prisoner of war" episode and was waiting to intercept Curly. Fatso saluted respectfully and said, "Commander, can I have a word with you?"

Curly, like everyone else on the ship, knew and respected Fatso. "Sure, fire away," he said.

"Commander," said Fatso, glancing sympathetically at Curly's nude pate, "I think they took unfair advantage of you over on the *Wilson*."

After you deleted all the four-letter Anglo-Saxon words from Curly's reply, it indicated general agreement with these sentiments.

"I know a way," said Fatso, "of getting back at Admiral Bell, in case you are interested."

"There's nothing in the world I'm more interested in," said Curly with some heat. "Lemme hear it."

Now, Hear This!

So Fatso proceeded to outline his long-cherished plan. "Commander," he said, "There's a little shop on the waterfront here where they rent all kinds of costumes for fancy dress balls and carnivals. Suppose you and me go ashore first thing in the morning before the *Wilson* gets in and suppose we . . . etc., etc."

When Fatso got through outlining his plan Curly was almost in hysterics. "It would be wonderful *if* it worked," said Curly. "It would go down in the naval history books."

"It can't *help* but work, Commander," said Fatso. He admitted that with any other admiral than Bugler Bell there might be a small chance of failure. But he pointed out that he *knew* Bugler from many sad years of service under him. Fatso assured Curly that daily routine events in each one of Bugler's thirty-five years of naval service had made him a pushover for the plan he had just unfolded. Fatso was a persuasive man and Curly agreed to go along with him.

"The only thing is, Commander," said Fatso, "we gotta be sure our admiral will back us up on this if necessary. After all, I'm due to retire pretty soon and you'll be coming up for 3 stripes before long. We wouldn't want to louse things up now."

"Yeah," said Curly, "I can see what you mean—I'll see our admiral about this this afternoon and let you know what he says."

Late that afternoon, Curly approached the admiral on the flag bridge. "Admiral," he said, "suppose I should go ashore and do something which is perfectly legal and doesn't violate any Navy regulations—"

"Have you ever succeeded in doing that yet?" the admiral asked.

"Maybe not recently," Curly said, "but anyway, suppose the people on the *Wilson* should see me doing this perfectly harmless something, should jump to a lot of false conclusions, and should do some things that eventually turn out to have been very silly?"

"I can easily imagine them doing that."

Monkey Business at Mers-el-Kebir

"Well," Curly said, "you understand that this might develop into quite a snafu, and the admiral and captain of the *Wilson* might become involved in it."

"A possibility which must be considered," the admiral said, with a gleam in his eyes.

"What I want to know, Admiral, is this—can anything happen to me and my helpers on account of this? I mean, while we are serving under your command?"

"Not a thing, my boy, not a solitary thing," the admiral said. "Ahem—Curly, perhaps we had better adjourn to my cabin and discuss this matter in greater detail."

Half an hour later, as Curly was leaving the cabin, Admiral Day said, "Remember now, I'm paying all the expenses for this party, but you'd better keep my name out of it, unless old 'Bugler' should get stuffy about it, in which case I'll chill the rap."

"Aye, aye, sir," Curly said, with a very military salute and very unmilitary wink.

The *Okinawa* made her way to Oran, where she tied up at the mole of Mers-el-Kebir. As the U.S.S. *Woodrow Wilson* proceeded toward Gibraltar, Admiral Bell was briefing his staff, giving them the broad picture of how he intended to run the Mediterranean after he took over command. He began with his estimate of the international situation, based on the latest intelligence reports. After discussing the emergency war plans, his policies in regard to training of the air groups and ships, and the necessity for all officers to avoid any political discussions ashore, he came to the last subject on his agenda—protocol, and ceremonial visits.

"This last item," he said, "may seem rather secondary in view of the global situation, but actually it is very important. Whenever we visit a friendly port for the first time, international custom requires an exchange of official visits with the mayor, the prefect, and the senior general and admiral. Whether I call on them first or they call on me depends on our relative rank. It's all laid down in detail in the regulation book. We must be very punctilious to see that when these officials call they are received in a manner that reflects credit on the United States. They must get exactly the proper honors—side boys, ruffles, flourishes, guns, and all the rest of it. I expect every one of you gentlemen to have that section of the regulations at his finger tips."

Turning to his flag lieutenant, he said, "Mr. Simpson, you are supposed to be the expert on all this. I will expect you to know all about foreign uniforms and personal flags so that when any of these dignitaries calls, we can recognize him at a distance and be ready to receive him with the appropriate ceremonies, whether it's an R.A.F. group captain or a Moslem prince."

"Aye, aye, sir," the flag lieutenant said nervously.

Next morning, when the *Wilson* anchored in Gibraltar, protocol oozed out of every porthole. Within two hours she was visited by a two-star admiral, a lieutenant general, an air vice-marshal, and the governor. Since they all necessarily came out by boat, it was easy to spot them coming, case them, and be prepared for them. Lieutenant Simpson took up his station on the signal bridge, and kept a big glass trained on the VIP landing. He scrutinized the personal flags which the various boats flew, looked them up in his book, and kept the Officer of the Deck informed of the rank of every approaching visitor.

The O.O.D. in turn, by merely consulting his table of honors in the U.S. Navy Regulations, was able to line up the correct number of side boys, instruct the bandmaster about ruffles and flourishes, and give the gunner his orders to fire the salute. By the time the visitors arrived, everything was in apple-pie order for them, and all the admiral, captain, and chief of staff had to do was to meet them at the gangway and escort them to the cabin.

The governor's reception particularly pleased Admiral Bell. The Boatswain's mate piped him aboard with just the right shrill notes and trills, the eight side boys saluting simultaneously on exactly

Monkey Business at Mers-el-Kebir

the right trill. The drummers rolled out the ruffles and the trumpeters blared forth the flourishes impressively. On the last flourish, the band broke promptly into the appropriate martial music and the Marines remained at a rigid present arms. When the governor inspected the guard, you could practically hear each Marine's eyeballs click as His Excellency strode by.

Two days later, the Wilson rounded the entrance buoy in Oran at 9:00 a.m. and headed for the inner harbor. Two hours earlier, Fatso and Lieutenant Commander Cue had gone ashore from the Okinawa looking like a couple of cats full of canaries au gratin.

Carriers do not anchor out at Oran. They come inside and tie up alongside the great mole of Mers-el-Kebir, a magnificent concrete pier which juts out one mile from the shore. The Okinawa was securely moored near the inshore end of the mole.

To come alongside the mole, it is necessary to make a sharp turn at the seaward end to avoid a sunken French battleship, and, on this particular morning, there was a spanking breeze blowing directly off the mole. The captain of the Wilson, handling his engines expertly, eased his huge ship in to within fifty feet of the mole and stopped her dead in the water abreast of her berth, nicely angled in at about fifteen degrees toward the dock.

On signal from the bridge, four French tugs stuck their noses against the Wilson's portside and began huffing and puffing to warp the ship alongside. A dozen line-throwing guns barked, and the little messenger lines sailed over to the dock, where the working parties from the Okinawa grabbed them and ran away with them, bringing over the bigger messenger lines.

Some heavy hauling on these lines soon dragged the great steel mooring cables from the ship to the mole. As the working parties dropped these cables in place on the bitts, the captain of the Wilson, well satisfied with his morning's work, said to his executive officer, "She's all yours, Commander. I'm going below." There was nothing left to do now but wait until heaving on the moor-

249

ing cables by the ship's winches and pushing by the tugs warped her in and laid her flat alongside the mole.

While all this was going on, Admiral Bell was in his cabin, shaving, looking forward to a quiet day of sight-seeing in Oran. Presumably, Admiral Day, on the *Okinawa*, had received and repaid all official calls upon his arrival two days before, so all Admiral Bell had to do was relax and enjoy himself.

At this point a shiny black Cadillac limousine tooled out on the mole from the Navy Yard at the inshore end. Lieutenant Simpson, up on the signal bridge surveying the scenery through the big glass, spotted it immediately and noted that it was flying what looked like the personal flag of a high official. Only mildly interested at first, he figured it was some big shot tardily repaying a call by Admiral Day of the *Okinawa*.

But the limousine rolled right past the *Okinawa*'s gangway, and the nattily uniformed driver brought it to a halt smack alongside the berth which the *Wilson* was being eased into. Gravely alarmed by now, Lieutenant Simpson took another quick gander through the glass at that personal flag. He could not make out for sure what it was, but it looked suspiciously like four stars, which calls for the works, so far as honors are concerned. Mr. Simpson promptly went to "Panic Stations" and started running in all directions at once. The *Wilson* at this moment was in no condition to render the works. The Marines were all in khaki instead of dress blues, the band was scattered all over the ship, and the gunner was probably asleep in his bunk.

The flag lieutenant clattered down the ladder to the bridge, rushed up to the executive and gasped, "For Gawd's sakes, Commander, get the full guard and band up to the starboard gangway right away."

Then he tumbled down three more ladders to warn the admiral. Bugles blew, bells rang, squawk boxes squawked, and the Marine top sergeant cursed as the alarm rang through the ship: "Now

Monkey Business at Mers-el-Kebir

hear this—lay aft the full guard and band on the double!"

The admiral, shaving in his cabin, took a nasty nick out of his chin as he heard this commotion and realized its obvious import. He was about to be called on. Before he could stop the flow of blood, Lieutenant Simpson came bounding in with his news and protested, "But Admiral Day was supposed to have taken care of this . . ."

"Don't stand there bellyaching about that," growled the admiral. "If this joker wants to call on me, I've got to receive him properly. Get things organized."

Two minutes later Admiral Bell hurried down the ladder to the quarter-deck with a big white patch on his chin. "Where's the captain and the chief of staff?" he demanded. "Get them down here. Where are the side boys?"

Everybody within earshot who had no immediate duties to perform drifted quietly out of sight. Everybody else saluted briskly and said, "Aye, aye, sir, right away, sir."

At this point the uniformed attendant opened the door of the limousine, and out stepped a distinguished-looking fat blue-clad figure wearing a cocked hat, sword, and epaulets, with gold braid up to his elbows, and full-dress aiguillettes on his shoulder.

Lieutenant Simpson clapped his spyglass on Fatso and announced, "That's only a two-star admiral, sir, not four. We only need six side boys instead of eight."

"Use your head, young man," growled Admiral Bell. "Can't you see the aiguillettes? He's just the aide. His boss hasn't got out of the car yet."

Verifying Admiral Bell's last statement, the blue-clad figure on the dock respectfully assisted what looked like the Caliph of all Islam out of the limousine. The alighting figure was an imposing character with a black beard, dressed in noble Arabic white silks, wearing a veiled turban, a jeweled scimitar, and more medals than you could count.

251

Now, Hear This!

"Oh, my Gawd," moaned Lieutenant Simpson. "I don't know what the hell honors we should give him!" Turning to the admiral, he offered him the spyglass. "Don't you want to take a look, Admiral?"

The admiral made a very rude suggestion as to what Lieutenant Simpson could do with the spyglass.

"Bugler!" shouted Bugler Bell. "Sound Attention to starboard!"

The bugle blared "Attention."

The two figures on the dock marched slowly to the edge of the mole, and gazed at the twenty feet of open water which still separated the *Wilson* from her berth. Then, after an inquiring glance toward the gangway, which was still triced up level with the hangar deck, they paced back to the limousine, did a military about-face, looked up at the quarter-deck, and assumed the position of parade rest.

The admiral glared at the captain and the chief of staff, who came clattering down the ladder at this point, and said, "Heave around on those lines. Tell those dago tugs to put their backs in it and push harder."

"Aye, aye, sir," the captain said.

Lieutenant Simpson had an inspiration. He walked smartly over to the rail and called down to the dock, "Attawn-syawn, Messieurs —parlez-vous français?"

The fat figure in blue shrugged politely and replied, "No spik Engleesh."

"I'm not speaking English—I'm parleying français," protested the flag lieutenant.

"Oh, shut up," ordered Admiral Bell. "Don't get rattled—but get those damn' Marines and the band up here quick."

The sheik, caliph, sultan, or whatever he was, now extended his arm in a regal gesture, pointing to the still unlowered gangway of the *Wilson.* He consulted his wrist watch ostentatiously, and turned to his aide with an inquiring tilt of his head. The aide shrugged his shoulders and spread his hands, and the pair of them began pacing back and forth impatiently along the dock.

"Lower the gangway," growled the admiral.

"But we're not alongside yet, sir," said the chief of staff.

"Lower it anyway! It may make them think we are doing something."

So down went the gangway with a run. It went a little too far— and before it could be hoisted up again, the extra heaving on the mooring lines and pushing of the tugs had shoved the ship into the dock, jamming the gangway between the side and the mole, and reducing its lower portion to splinters.

The sultan and his naval aide gazed first at the shattered gangway, then at the spell-bound crowd on the quarter-deck, then at each other, and shook their heads sadly.

After a number of irrelevant observations, Admiral Bell's years of handling tense situations in the Pentagon came to the rescue, and he got control of himself.

By this time a dozen or so Marines, a couple of piccolo players, and the big bass drummer were hastily forming ranks on the quarter-deck.

"All hands shift to the after gangway," the admiral said between clenched teeth. "Mr. Simpson, will you please explain to that Frenchman that we will receive him a hundred yards further aft."

As the Marines and musicians scrambled aft, the Sheik of Islam tapped the French admiral on his starboard epaulet, gestured dramatically at his wrist watch, sneered in the direction of the gangway, and pointed imperiously to the open door of the limousine. The admiral clicked his heels, saluted smartly and got ready to re-embark in the Cadillac. His Islamic Majesty then placed his thumb to his nose, waggled his fingers in a strangely un-Moslemlike gesture, and, removing his turban and beard, made a sweeping bow to the admiral, captain, and chief of staff, revealing a freshly cropped and unmistakable red head.

Now, Hear This!

His Curly Highness and Fatso then leaped into the limousine and got the hell off that mole.

A half-hour after these events had transpired, Curly Cue and Fatso returned to the *Okinawa* in their proper U.S. Navy uniforms. Curly immediately headed for the admiral's cabin and Fatso for the incinerator.

In the cabin Curly found Admiral Day still in a state of semi-hysterics from the scene he witnessed through the big glass on the signal bridge. "Curly," he said between guffaws, "it was the funniest thing I've seen since when I was an ensign and the captain got one foot caught in the bight of a boat fall when they were lowering away and got two-blocked at the davit upside down, bellowing at the top of his lungs."

"Yessir," said Curly, "it came off pretty well."

"It was worth every minute of thirty-five years' hard naval service," agreed the admiral.

"And—uh—sir—I assume you will take care of any legal repercussions, sir?"

"Don't you worry about that m'boy," said the admiral. "It's going to be difficult. But after all I'm two numbers senior to the Bugler and we're sailing for the U.S. tomorrow. I'll fix it."

Down in the incinerator Fatso was giving his cronies a full run-down on the affair. Usually, in relating his adventures, Fatso gilded the lily a bit but this one was beyond even Fatso's great talent to gild. He just told the boys exactly what had happened and rolled them in the aisles.

At the end of his saga, Beer Bottle summed up the sentiments of all hands: "It was even better than that time at the Mardi Gras parade when the gendarme clobbered the old lady."

"Yep," said Fatso. "I think it was. The way old Bugler Bell made them tugs slam that ship into the dock reminded me of the way he used to bring the *Yorktown* alongside. And now that I've squared accounts with him I can retire with a clean conscience."

254